THE LONGEVITY HANDBOOK

T H E
LONGEVITY
HANDBOOK

Flying Crane Kung

SHENG KENG YUN

SAMUEL WEISER, INC.
York Beach, Maine

First published in 1999 by
SAMUEL WEISER, INC.
Box 612
York Beach, ME 03910-0612
www.weiserbooks.com

Library of Congress Cataloging-in-Publication Data

Sheng, Keng Yun.
    The longevity handbook : flying crane kung /
Sheng Keng Yun.
        p. cm.
    Includes index.
    ISBN 1-57863-108-4 (pbk. : alk. paper)
        1. Ch'i kung--Handbooks, manuals, etc. 2. Exercise--
    Handbooks, manuals, etc. 3. Longevity--Handbooks,
    manuals, etc. I. Title.
    RA781.8.S5349 1999   98-55722
    613.7'148--dc21   CIP

VG
Typeset in 10pt Diotima
Cover and text design by Kathryn Sky-Peck
Cover painting by Yuan Xiaocen, a hanging scroll given
to the author by the artist.

PRINTED IN THE UNITED STATES OF AMERICA
06 05 04 03 02 01 00 99
7 6 5 4 3 2 1

To the memory of my father and mother. My father, a Taoist, inspired me to study Ch'i Kung and Tai Ch'i Ch'uan when I was very young. He often brought me to watch Tai Ch'i Ch'uan and I have many happy memories of this time in my life. My mother was a Buddhist and taught me the vegetarian lifestyle. Both parents taught me to be kind to people, to help people when they faced difficulties and to live a life that benefited others. I have followed my parents' advice and thank them for showing me this path.

PUBLISHER'S NOTE

The author and publisher of this material are not responsible in any manner whatsoever for any injury caused directly or indirectly by reading or following the instructions in this text. The physical and psychological activities described in the text may be too strenuous for some people. Readers should consult a qualified physician before engaging in these, or any other, exercises.

If you have a medical condition, or are of uncertain health, immediately seek attention and advice from a qualified medical doctor. Although the practice of Ch'i Kung is beneficial in many instances, it is neither a diagnostic tool nor an exclusive treatment for pathological conditions. Ch'i Kung can be used to complement, but not replace, a doctor's care.

CONTENTS

ACKNOWLEDGMENTS

I am grateful to Professor Robert Kohls, to my Attorney-at-Law, Gary Dulberg, and to Judith Faria: they all gave me wonderful support when I was writing this book.

PREFACE

Why I Learned Ch'i Kung

Smile once,
ten years younger you will be.
Be sorrowful once in your heart,
White hair you will see.
— CHINESE PROVERB

I began to study Ch'i Kung because, while in my 20s, I almost died from an illness that doctors could not seem to cure. My blood pressure reached 200 mm hg systolic and 130 mm hg diastolic. I could not sleep, I could not sit up or walk, I could barely talk, and I was simply without energy. My family took me out of the hospital because neither Western nor traditional Chinese therapies had helped me, and the doctors said I was going to die. Helpless as I was, unable to move, my life was saved by practicing Ch'i Kung under a master's direction.

The question of why I learned Ch'i Kung awakens memories of many, many things that have happened in my life.

I was very healthy and athletic growing up in Kunming, which is in the Yunnan Province in southwestern China. I pursued basketball, gymnastics, and volleyball, and became familiar with Ch'i Kung and Tai Ch'i because of my father's interest in them. I came from a middle-class capitalist family; my parents owned some fields in the countryside near Kunming, and they operated two shops in the city. My father was a Taoist and my mother was a Buddhist. My father always stressed the importance of education; he saw to it that I learned classic Chinese from a private tutor starting when I was 4 years old.

I studied English throughout primary school, junior and senior middle schools, and the university. During my school years I studied hard, earned high marks, and won prizes in both academic and athletic sports courses. I was happy to expand my education, as my father had always encouraged me to do.

In 1949, I graduated from Yunnan University in foreign languages and literature. Because of China's close ties with Russia at the time, there was much demand for Russian speakers, but Yunnan University did not offer Russian, so I was sent to the Institute of Foreign Language at Harbin, in far-off northeast China, where I studied Russian for two years. When I returned, I began to teach Russian at Yunnan University.

Because of the great demand to learn Russian, I quickly became overloaded with courses; I was obliged to teach four courses at three levels, each course requiring different preparation. I was under constant stress and never had time to relax. After a year of this feverish pace I fell ill, suffering from hypertension, rheumatism, neurasthenia, and fears. This was the first time I had ever been seriously ill.

My father invited a famous Buddhist Ch'i Kung master to come to our house to teach me the ancient practice of Ch'i Kung. I remember being excited at the prospect of meeting Master Chang, and I can recall very vividly our first encounter. He was wearing a red robe and had a long gray beard.

He said to me: "If you believe Ch'i Kung, you will be healed; but if you do not believe, then I can do nothing." I could only nod my head that I believed.

Because I was too weak to move, Master Chang started by teaching me "Quiet Kung," which is a form of meditation consisting of various disciplines. I practiced while lying in bed. Master Chang came to see me every day, and corrected any mistakes I was making in my practice.

At first, it was almost impossible for me to practice Ch'i Kung since I was unable to quiet my mind. My mind ceaselessly worried about dying, wondered what would happen to my possessions, who was teaching my classes instead of me, and so on. Gradually, however, I learned to concentrate. I slowly was able to sit up, to sleep at night, and could walk across the room. After a year, my condition had greatly improved, and I decided that I wanted to learn more about Ch'i Kung.

Shortly after Master Chang's helping my medical condition so greatly, I was told that a Tibetan Buddhist Ch'i Kung master would be in Kunming. He was a famous Tibetan Buddhist monk named Lin Gar Den Ba. When he first came, several hospitals invited him to lecture. His lectures were unique and he was able to help people improve their health.

Following the lectures, he let some Ch'i Kung masters practice his Ch'i Kung. What I saw was way beyond my imagination. One man, lying on a table, began to have spontaneous movements. Gradually, his body, at first reclining on the table, slowly floated above the table—sometimes high, sometimes low. I was dumbfounded at this sight.

Lin Gar Den Ba belonged to the Mi Chion sect of Buddha. Monks from the Mi Chion sect wear different colored robes to represent the various levels of Mi Chion attainment. The colors are yellow, red, white, and mixed colors. Because he was in red robes, it was clear he belonged to the second class. It might also be of interest to note that Mi Chion Buddhists sometimes include chicken in their diet, whereas some other Buddhist strictly exclude all meat because of their interest in preserving all forms of living, sentient beings.

Although he was about 90 years old, Lin Gar Den Ba's face was the rose-pink color of a baby. He looked like an elder gentleman, but he walked quickly, animatedly—not like an old man. He was very kind and benevolent. He not only researched the philosophy of Buddha, but also studied classical Chinese. He was a learned man, a writer, and a poet.

After attending a lecture, I learned that Lin Gar Den Ba would be visiting the Huating Temple at Dian Chi Lake near Kunming. I asked my friend, Chen Yion Chin, to go with me to see him. Ms. Chen and I were suffering the same sickness. We hoped to ask him to heal it.

My friend and I had a mental conflict. We were longing to meet him and hoping he could cure our sickness, but we were both somewhat afraid, partly an effect of the medical condition. We talked to each other about our fears and dislikes and this made us even more pessimistic and fearful.

Early in the morning, in spite of our fears, we took the bus that went directly to the Huating Temple. So far, we felt fine. We climbed up the west mountain to the top to reach the Temple. We found Lin Gar Den Ba's room, which was quiet and clean, and entered into it. As soon as we saw him we felt more peaceful and relaxed. We told him we had come to visit him. Without speaking, he had us sit down with him. Then he poured us a cup of fresh spring water and began to write this poem with a brush. When it was done, he gave it to me.

> *With your friend, Chen Yion Chin,*
> *You visit me on the Western Mountains.*
> *Your spirit is heavy with illness;*
> *Lightness and tranquility come with courage.*
> *One cup of clear spring water will wash away*
>   *your worries.*

In the beginning, you had no sickness,
Yet now you knit your eyebrows.

After I read his poem, I thought that maybe I was cured of sickness, but I still had discomfort in my back and suffered from persistent fears. I told him about myself, and he told me that I needed to be brave. Obviously, Lin Gar Den Ba had immediately recognized my state; I was not yet completely well.

Chen Yion Chin and I stayed at this temple for about a week. The first night, we stayed in a room directly beneath Lin Gar Den Ba's room. In the middle of the night, my fears overcame me, and I cried out loudly. Lin Gar Den Ba heard me and knocked on the floor. He called out to me, "Don't cry!" Then, without leaving his room, he told me in a loud voice, "Turn onto your right side, straighten your right leg, bend your left leg on top of it, and sleep so that your hands will not press on your heart." Following his instructions, I was able to sleep soundly the rest of the night. What he had taught me was the very wonderful "Ru Lei Buddha's Sleeping Posture." From that time to the present, I sleep according to what he taught me, using "Ru Lei Buddha's Sleeping Posture," so that nothing resembling the terrible crying out loudly at midnight will ever happen to me again.

The next morning Lin Gar Den Ba began to teach me Mi Chion Ch'i Kung, "Conquer the Devil Kung," or "Ch'i Kung of Conquering the Devil," which was for the specific problem I had. He taught me to be brave and to drive away my fears by repeating a secret Buddhist mantra: "On . . . Ah . . . Hon."

The posture was as follows. Lift up the right foot, so you are standing on the ground with the left foot. Raise up the right hand with "Arrow Fingers." (Bend the ring finger and the little finger, putting the thumb on their nails, keeping the middle finger and index finger out straight.) Let the left hand hang naturally at the left side. When the posture is set, then repeat "On, Ah, Hon" several times. When the sound of my voice seemed to surround me, gradually I would develop a brave feeling; then I shouted loudly "Pei!" while at the same time stamping my right foot heavily on the ground. It seemed that all the devils ran away; I felt relaxed, quiet, and comfortable, and became brave and happy. Although this Kung may sound silly to you, it really helped me overcome my fears; I practiced it for months whenever I became afraid. Eventually my fears disappeared for good.

He taught each of us Kungs that were for specific problems or illnesses we had. Another Kung he taught me was to strengthen my kidneys, for in traditional Chinese medicine, a weak kidney will cause a person to be fearful and timid. In the "Eight Lotus Petal Kung," I would imagine an inverted lotus flower with eight petals, and on each petal, crystal-clear water would gather into a droplet and fall off the petal tip.

During our visit more than a hundred Buddhist monks and nuns were also gathered at Huating Temple. It was their Buddhist festival time. They came from different temples in Yunnan in the southwest of China. They repeated their Buddhist scripture, one after another, accompanied by harmonious Buddhist music. During that period of time, the whole temple, even all the mountains, became quiet. We could hear nothing but the repeat of Buddhist scripture. It was wonderful, this splendid Huating Temple among the mountains! It made a very deep impression on me; one that has lasted all my life.

My friend and I took walks with our great Ch'i Kung master, Lin Gar Den Ba, and enjoyed the beauties of nature near the temple. Before we left, we joined the monks in a delicious vegetarian banquet.

Shortly after our stay at the temple, Lin Gar Den Ba went to the Kan Fu Hospital near Kunming to teach Ch'i Kung to the patients there. Chen Yion Chin and I went there to study with him. I learned many forms of Ch'i Kung from him during my studies there.

Lin Gar Den Ba taught us what he called "Natural Meditation," a form of Quiet Kung. He would take us for walks when the weather was fine, and we would each take along a small wooden stool. When we would reach a beautiful spot, we would stop and sit for about an hour, quietly absorbing all the experiences of nature, keeping our eyes open and ourselves receptive. When we returned to the hospital, we would meditate with our eyes closed, and recall all the beauty and peace of our walk. He told us to let the scenery that made us most happy live in our minds.

One year after I met Lin Gar Den Ba, I had completely recovered. My hypertension was gone, I was healthy and vigorous again, and I was able to rest well. My whole life was changed; I was delighted with the effects of Ch'i Kung.

I decided to devote myself to mastering it and teaching it to as many people as possible. I realized what a priceless heritage Ch'i Kung is.

I spent the next four years traveling and learning many different forms of Ch'i Kung and Tai Ch'i. I went to Suchow, Beijing, Hangchow, Shanghai, and Nanjing, and studied with many famous masters. I learned many forms of Ch'i Kung and several styles of Tai Ch'i. Afterward, I returned to Kunming, to the Yunnan University, and took up my foreign language teaching duties, meanwhile continuing to practice and study Ch'i Kung in my spare time.

While I was in Kunming, I learned "Golden Veined Lotus Leaf Floating Over Water" from Pon Chian Chien, who was a great Ch'i Kung master. He had studied Ch'i Kung at a temple of Ta Li County in Yunnan for about 30 years before he came to Kunming to teach.

Early every morning, at the Square, many people were already standing, prepared to welcome the great master's coming. After he arrived, he would ceaselessly teach and practice, while all of us imitated him. Our hands and feet followed his, moving gently and harmoniously. We did not feel tired, even though we usually practiced about two hours without stopping. He taught us "Golden Veined Lotus Leaf Floating Over Water" and "Eight Immortals Kung." I also learned other sets of Ch'i Kung from him. In addition to working with the group, he gave me private lessons.

Now this master is very well-known. In an article describing the Chinese Scientific Academic Meeting held in October, 1987 at Xian, Great Master Pon Chian Chien, who represented Yunnan, Western China, was a special guest. His demonstrations were exceptionally appealing and he attracted quite an audience. More than 80 years old, this Ch'i Kung master wore a very beautiful long red robe. His very healthy condition, his light step, and his rose-pink face, all of these, won the affection of the audience.

He demonstrated the highest forms of Mi Chion Ch'i Kung: "Eighteen Lo Han Worshipping Kwan Yin," "Tai Yang Kung (Sun Kung)," "Different Fragrant Spirits Kung," and so on. His movements were quick, complicated, and changeable, some hard, some soft, some light, some heavy, some slow, some rapid. This form is very different from Quiet Kung, which is performed in a natural state.

While I was still in Kunming, I also learned from an elder military general. He was a very good Tai Ch'i Ch'uan master who liked teaching what he knew to anybody who wished to learn from him at the Green Lake Park in Kunming.

Why would an elder military general become an ordinary Tai Ch'i Ch'uan master? One early morning in the Green Lake Park, when some people were gathered around him to listen to all his comments, I was standing by his side when he answered with this story.

During the Japanese and Chinese War, all the soldiers, military officers, and generals would take a rest for a while after each battle. Before daybreak one day, three generals were walking in the forest in the northeast of China. Among the trees they suddenly noticed something shaking that aroused their interest. They quietly walked closer to it

hoping to see what it was, but as they got closer, it disappeared. They could find nothing that would have caused
such a phenomenon. How strange it was, they thought.

Afterward, they decided to come to the same place
again the next morning to see if they could find out what
it was. In the thick forest they could only watch the shadow moving. When the three of them walked nearer, the
shadow again quickly disappeared. The more they could
not see it, the more curious they became.

At last they determined to go earlier, each approaching
from a different direction. The shadow was already there.
This time they walked very carefully and quietly.

What appeared before them was an old man with a
long white beard. He was seriously practicing martial arts.
They politely talked with him and asked him, "What is the
use of your long pole?"

He promptly answered them, "To defeat the enemy!"

They asked him, "How could you defeat the enemy
with a pole?"

He handed his pole to one of them and asked the general to beat him. At first, the general dared not beat him.
The old man cried loudly, "Don't be afraid. Quickly, with
strength, beat me!"

So the general tried, thinking to himself, "The man is
so old; I must be careful not to hurt him." The other two
watched. Many times the general tried, but his pole could
not touch the old man. One by one, all three of them
tried. No one could beat him. After that, they asked him if
he would teach them, and he agreed to do so. They

learned several sets of martial arts, including "Ru Yi Tai Ch'i Ch'uan."

The name we had been given for it when we began to learn it was "168." One of the general's students wished to know its original name, so he researched "168" in the library. Two weeks later he told us the original name of "168" is "Ru Yi Tai Ch'i Ch'uan," from which derived many kinds of Tai Ch'i Ch'uan, e.g., Yang Style, Wu Style, Chen Style, Bar Gua Tai Ch'i, Monkey Ch'uan, Drunken Ch'uan, and Shin Yi Ch'uan, plus many others. I like "Ru Yi Tai Ch'i Ch'uan" and have spent a lot of time learning and practicing it.

In 1967, I began to study Taoist Ch'i Kung with another very prominent master who is now a vigorous and healthy 108 years old. I learned a great many forms of Ch'i Kung from him.

He requested that his students not take notes as they learned; he said that it was more important to learn the forms from memory. He also asked us: "If the student should lose his written notes, and another person should find them and practice them wrongly, thus injuring himself, who would take responsibility for this situation?"

With reference to giving knowledge, he said that if it was truth, it would take only a few sentences; if it was false, it might take many books.

I recall fondly an incident when a fly landed on his granddaughter's nose when she was practicing. She was about to brush it off when, with a rapid movement, he hit her hand and instructed that when you are practicing a non-moving Kung, you do *not* move. You should highly concentrate your consciousness on it.

He was very strict and highly disciplined. He and his wife, as well, are models of what he teaches. They both continue to rise very early every morning to practice Ch'i Kung for a few hours.

Although he came from a wealthy family, whose large buildings occupied the space of two streets, and he had no need for money, he and his wife live very simply in modest surroundings. He has a noble character and philosophy which he constantly follows. He exemplifies one of my favorite proverbs.

> *Even if one owns ten thousand hectares of fertile fields,*
> *he can eat only three meals a day.*
> *Even if one owns thousands of splendid buildings,*
> *he needs no more than eight feet of space for*
> *sleeping at night.*
> —CHINESE PROVERB

According to his wishes, I cannot mention his name here.

One of the forms of Ch'i Kung I learned from this Great Master is a most powerful Taoist Kung called "Without Desire." The Kung is one in which you let all desires drop away and let your mind become empty, so that your mind can sufficiently take rest. In this way, true Ch'i will be produced.

When you practice, you may sit on a chair without a back, the soles of your feet are on the ground, the thighs and lower legs form 90-degree angles. The backs of both your hands are placed on your upper legs with palms upward. The tip of the tongue touches the hard palate. You are relaxed. (You may cross your legs while sitting on the chair, but usually it is better to use the former posture to practice.) Then you should empty and quiet your mind.

When I began to practice, I could not let my mind become empty; disturbances and confusion always appeared. As I tried to drive one thought out of my mind, another would emerge. So I would try to drive it away. After a little while, there would finally be none, but then yet another new disturbance would turn up. I knew I should be patient and tried simply to let it go away. In this way, practicing patiently, eventually many disturbances in my mind slowly became smaller and less important. Each time following my practice of this Taoist Kung, I felt very comfortable, relaxed, and rejuvenated.

This kind of Kung is easy to practice, but it is not easy to let your mind become empty. When your mind really does become empty, you will feel very, very comfortable and vitalized. Above all, your mind is refreshed. This Kung is very beneficial to your health.

This same Great Master also taught me "Sun Kung." Before 12 o'clock in the morning, I stood outside and looked at the Sun. At the beginning, the Sun seemed to have blue and red colors. Gradually, it became clearer. Around the sun there is a circle, whose colors are blue and red, sometimes purple, which can appear to jump and float when you stare at it.

The Great Master emphasized the importance of the following. When you stand facing the Sun, you must let your hands rest on your waist vertebrae, with your thumbs touching your kidneys, and the four fingers pointing to the front. The reason involves the five-element theory. He explained that the kidneys belong to the water element, but the Sun belongs to the fire element—so that when fire meets water, the whole body can adjust and be in balance. Thus, this practice will benefit your eyes, not hurt them, and also improve your vision. I did it according to what he taught, and it assuredly has been very good for my eyes. But do not do this without a master to teach you!

During the Cultural Revolution in China, I went from Kunming to Suzhow, Hangchow, Shanghai, and Nanjing looking for famous and very good Ch'i Kung and Tai Ch'i Ch'uan masters from whom I could learn. I met more than ten masters and learned many sets from them.

When I was in Shanghai in 1970, in Chia Bei Park, I learned several sets of Tai Ch'i Ch'uan from Fu Chon Wen, who is the nephew of Yang Chen Pu. Yang Chen Pu was a creator of the Yang Style of Tai Ch'i Ch'uan. For about three years I learned from Fu Chon Wen.

When I recall the period of the Cultural Revolution, I remember that most of my time was spent in the park; sometimes I was there the entire day, learning, practicing, and watching others practice. In fact, every day I studied from Ch'i Kung books and magazines. My knowledge of Ch'i Kung increased and I enjoyed my study.

Then, in 1977, I began to research medical Ch'i Kung

which, using the principles of traditional Chinese medicine, seeks to improve health and vigor, prevent and treat diseases, and increase longevity.

I have devoted more than a third of my life to learning, researching, practicing, and teaching various forms of Ch'i Kung and Tai Ch'i Ch'uan. They are wonderful and powerful gifts to humankind from the Chinese culture. I have gained so much from them that I would like to contribute all I know to the people who are interested in these gifts. It is true that if a person practices Ch'i Kung diligently, it will help him or her to live a healthy and happy life.

I taught in San Francisco, California, at the San Francisco School of Chinese Medicine, San Francisco State University, and the American College of Traditional Chinese Medicine for a number of years. In my classes, I was able to teach in both Chinese and English, which was very helpful for my students. According to their needs, I taught students at their own level, teaching different sets to different people. I paid close attention to the progress of each student's individual health condition. After practice, even from the very first day, I asked students to write about how they felt before and after practice. Thus, I now have a collection of many reports written by students. Almost everyone, regardless of their condition at the beginning, seriously ill or not, has shown improvement from practicing Ch'i Kung.

I enjoy seeing people eagerly and diligently practicing Ch'i Kung. They are learning that, first of all, even before beginning practice, their state of mind must be relaxed, tranquil, and in a natural state. Then they can start to practice.

They are also learning that immediately following their practice of Ch'i Kung, they may be able to remain relaxed, quiet, and in a natural state at least for a short time. This is beneficial. The longer they remain in that state, the more beneficial it is.

Eventually they would ask if they could keep their minds continuously relaxed and quiet and in a natural state. Some people are highly concentrated when they practice Ch'i Kung, but when they finish they forget and revert to their former state of mind. They cannot keep their minds in the state in which it was when they were practicing the Kung. Even merely seeing something that makes them unhappy will cause them to lose their temper or become angry. When this happens, it is difficult to say what benefits they received from practicing Ch'i Kung.

A few Ch'i Kung masters suggest practicing Ch'i Kung 24 hours a day. You might wonder how this could be possible. It means that you should always allow the mind to be constantly relaxed, quiet, and in a natural state. It is not very easy to achieve this.

First of all, in order to practice Ch'i Kung 24 hours a day, it is necessary to allow yourself to help others. Be faithful and honest with people. In this way, when you practice Ch'i Kung, your mind is easily relaxed and disturbances are easily removed from your mind. The effect of practicing Ch'i Kung is very deep and far-reaching, so it is important to cultivate your virtue at all times.

Some people who suffer from chronic diseases want to find a Ch'i Kung master to emit Ch'i to cure the sickness instantly. This is one method, but it provides only a temporary cure for their problem. A better method is to actually practice Ch'i Kung, for the practice offers permanent and lasting effects.

To examine whether or not this is true, consider the fact that every person gets older day by day. Naturally, this is more noticeable in middle-aged and older people. If they would engage in practicing Ch'i Kung every day for themselves, it would daily benefit their muscles and bones, improve their immune system, digestive system, respiratory system, blood circulation system, and their nervous system. What a difference Ch'i Kung can make!

If you hope to get good results and everlasting effects from practicing Ch'i Kung, you must continuously practice it, not just for one month or one year, but all your life. This is the most important word of advice I can give to you.

May people

　　practicing Ch'i Kung

　　soar into the sky!

May people

　　practicing Ch'i Kung

　　have a crane's long-life!

—YUAN XIAO CHIN,
CHINA, 1986

如
鶴之翔如鶴之壽
一九八六年袁曉岑

part one

CH'I KUNG AND HEALTH

WHAT IS CH'I KUNG?

*"When one is completely indifferent to fame or fortune,
genuine vital energy (Ch'i) will become part of him.*

*When one concentrates his consciousness internally,
how can diseases attack him?"*

—HUANG TI NEI JING

L iterally, *Ch'i* means "air" or "breath," it is pronounced
"chee"; and *Kung* means "working of," pronounced
"goong." According to the Pinyin System of Chinese
writing, we use "Qigong," but in this book I have chosen to
use "Ch'i Kung," because it is easier for Westerners to pro-
nounce, since they are more familiar with the older Wade
Giles System of translating Chinese.

Ch'i refers to the vital energy present in all living things.
Thus, Ch'i Kung literally means the working of air or breath,
but it is more complicated than this; it refers to the work-

ing of the invisible vital energy in the human body. Ch'i is the vital energy that animates all organisms; you cannot live without Ch'i. It is found wherever there is life: from the moment of conception to the moment just before death, Ch'i is present, being consumed and constantly being replenished. It is present wherever there is movement. Ch'i is the source of growth and vigor in all living things, including plants, animals, and micro-organisms. There is no exact equivalent to the concept of Ch'i in Western science. However, Chinese scientists regard Ch'i as a substantial material that has been objectively verified to exist. Ch'i Kung is the internal function of conscious thought, which is the highest stage of activity in the cerebral cortex.

Usually Ch'i Kung is considered to be a skill for strengthening health, and it is practiced all over China. It plays an active role in preventing and treating diseases, resisting premature aging, and prolonging life. That is why Ch'i Kung was called the method "to eliminate diseases and prolong life" in China.

There are many kinds of Ch'i Kung. For example, in ancient times, "Tao Ying" was a practice that used movement, respiration, and imagination to guide the spirit to combine with the body as one. Another ancient practice, "Tu Na" (exhaling and inhaling), is a kind of self-exertion trained by consciously controlling respiration. "Tian Ch'i" is used to train the vital energy. Sitting quietly is a kind of Quiet Kung that is enriched by further practice to enter into a state of complete quietness (the tranquility of the mind). "Moving Kung" is another method in which you are trained to combine tranquility and movement together. "Zhuang Kung" is a training method in which you stand quietly. There is even a "Walking Kung," which is used to cure cancer in China, but it also helps to cure many other kinds of diseases.[1]

Nowadays Ch'i Kung is becoming more familiar in the West. It is considered to be a technique to train your body and heart. Here, heart refers to virtue or character, rather than to the physical organ. Ch'i Kung is also a technique for cultivating wisdom because it has electrical, mathematical, chemical, and biological effects on the mind and body. From this point of view, modern scientists research Ch'i Kung, which is closely related with the social sciences and with natural science.

What is Ch'i?

People always associate Ch'i with air. Ch'i includes air in its definition, but Ch'i must embody other meanings as well, for it is used in the term "Ch'i Kung."

According to scientific experiments, the Ch'i released by a Ch'i Kung master who is skilled in the art of Ch'i Kung contains infrared radiation, static electricity, and particle streams, etc. Ch'i in the Ch'i Kung state is highly relaxed, tranquil, and in the natural state of being. Ch'i creates its own message or energy, together with its carrier. It is believed that the Ch'i carrier is a kind of "substance" and

1. Students may wish to refer to Sheng Keng Yun, *Walking Kung* (York Beach, ME: Samuel Weiser, 1997).

that this substance exists objectively. So the Ch'i in Ch'i Kung not only means inhaling oxygen and exhaling carbon dioxide, it also indicates a kind of substance that possesses a rich message and energy of its own.

In ancient times people considered this Ch'i to be the natural substance that originally made up the world, the universe. All kinds of changes were thought to depend upon Ch'i.

In traditional Chinese medicine Ch'i is usually called "true Ch'i" or "Yuan Ch'i," and is differentiated from the air breathed in and out. The theory of traditional Chinese medicine holds that the true Ch'i of the human body is the motivating force of all its vital activities. Therefore, the building up of Ch'i, in terms of Ch'i Kung, refers to the building up of true Ch'i. So in traditional Chinese medicine Ch'i is the basic substantial material that makes up the human body. This explains all the activities of life since all activities involve the moving and changing of Ch'i. So it is said: "If a person is alive, it depends completely on Ch'i." And it is also said: "If Ch'i is gathered together, a person will be formed; if Ch'i is scattered, the person will disappear as if he is dead." There is an old proverb: "Whether a person is alive or not only depends on a mouthful of Ch'i." That is, if a person is without Ch'i, he or she will be dead.

Ch'i may be classified into four types. The first is original Ch'i (Yuan Ch'i). It is also called prenatal Ch'i, transmitted by parents to their children at the time of conception. The Ch'i is obtained from the parents when the fetus is forming. This is why it is said that Ch'i denotes the fundamental matter and motivating force that maintains the physiological functions of the body's tissues and organs. This Ch'i is partly responsible for an individual's inherited constitution. It is stored in the kidneys.

The second type of Ch'i is "Tson Ch'i" (Lung's Ch'i). Traditional Chinese medicine considers that the chest gathers together Tson Ch'i, which supports the lung's breath and the blood circulation of the heart. It is said: "If one does not eat for half a day, the Ch'i will become weak. If one does not eat for one day, the Ch'i will be reduced even more." This means that Tson Ch'i in the chest may be nourished by breathing in the perfect Ch'i of the universe, yet it is also important to supply the body with food. Tson Ch'i is not only the guiding principle of the lung's breath, but also the general outline of the blood's circulation, thus effecting the whole body.

The third is "Yun Ch'i" (stomach Ch'i). In the stomach Yun Ch'i's function is to nourish the whole body. Yun Ch'i plays a role of helping the stomach move, digest food, and expel waste material. Yun Ch'i also moves up and down; this is caused by breathing. If the stomach is without Ch'i, it becomes empty. Then the food you eat cannot go down. When you are suffering from liver disease, heart disease, and stomach disease, the stagnant Ch'i in the stomach makes you uncomfortable. If you use Ch'i Kung to help cure these kinds of diseases, the exercise itself produces a more favorable form of breathing. The diaphragm descends and the abdominal wall protrudes during inhaling and the reverse movements occur during exhaling.

The fourth type of Ch'i is "We Ch'i" (intestinal Ch'i). Traditional Chinese medicine believed that We Ch'i comes from the body taking in good food. We Ch'i is similar to Yun Ch'i: both come from water and grain. But We Ch'i is in the intestines. Its function is to protect various organs of the abdomen, and to urge the intestines to move, to digest and absorb oxygen, and to push the stool out of the body. It also expels carbon dioxide out of the body. Yun Ch'i and We Ch'i not only function to nourish the body, they also protect the body.

A person's internal Ch'i is like the tires of a car or a truck. If the tires are without Ch'i, they become deflated. They cannot move the vehicle even though it has enough gasoline in it and the engine is in perfect order. When the tires are inflated, there will be sufficient Ch'i inside the tires, and even though the car is filled with a heavy load, it can easily go a long distance. From this example you can see that your internal Ch'i is important for the efficient functioning of the body. In traditional Chinese medicine the doctors consider: "If a person is without Ch'i, it is very difficult to step one inch forward."

There is not a single spot inside the entire body that does not have Ch'i; there is no place where Ch'i does not penetrate. Ch'i is constantly moving within the body, and it moves in major directions—ascending, descending, entering, and leaving. The *Nei Jing* states: "Without entering and leaving, there is no development, without ascending and descending, no transformation, absorption, and storing." Normal physiological activity is Ch'i moving fluently in all the proper directions. If there is insufficient Ch'i, or if any of the Ch'i directions lose their regulation and the Ch'i cannot flow freely through every part of the body, then the person will become ill.

The *Nei Jing* also states: "There are seven emotions that particularly affect the body." For example, excessive joy can scatter the heart Ch'i, causing the spirit to sometimes become uncomfortable, uncontrolled, and even to make the person muddle-headed. When excessive anger affects the liver, there may be signs, such as dizziness, chest congestion, a bitter taste in the mouth, or pain in the upper abdomen and sides. Sadness or grief may weaken the lung Ch'i, while great fear can make the kidney Ch'i descend, even sometimes making a person lose control of urination. Excessive pensiveness may result in stagnation of the Ch'i, thereby disturbing the spleen's function of transforming food and leading to such abdominal symptoms as stomach distention or poor digestion.

Ch'i is the basic underlying principle of traditional Chinese medicine, but no English word or phrase has exactly the same meaning.

What is Kung?

Kung means the time and quality of practicing Ch'i Kung. Kung also means the learning of the methodology and the attainment of the skill necessary for successfully practicing Ch'i Kung. In short, Kung is the method by which you build up Ch'i. Through Ch'i Kung practice, true Ch'i is made to function normally and exuberantly inside the human body—this is the meaning of Kung. How can you make the vital energy inside the human body increase and be exuberant?

First of all, you must have confidence, then determination and perseverance. Lacking any one of these, it is very difficult to produce good results. If you have solid confidence, unwavering determination, and steadfast perseverance, you will be able to improve your skill of practicing Ch'i Kung and good results will follow. If you have sufficient vital energy, you will have excellent health.

The building up of Ch'i involves three techniques: first—to breathe essential and vital Ch'i; second—to maintain a quiescent mental state; third—to keep the body organs functioning harmoniously. These three techniques are aimed at tempering the "focus of thought," "the breath," and "the configuration," which are known as the three essential factors of Ch'i Kung. These three techniques regulate the body and the heart, create the condition of quietness, and regulate breathing.

When practicing Ch'i Kung, you should be relaxed, quiet, and in a natural state. You should also concentrate your conscious thought on one point of the body. In general, this would be the "Dan Tian" (three finger-widths below the navel).[2] When you concentrate on this area, numerous tiny particles are emitted. Ch'i from the Dan Tian radiates "Yi Zhen" behind the skull. Where the energy of the Ch'i

---

2 See glossary for an explanation of Dan Tian.

emerges, there are burning, crystal-like silk-light drops. These light drops are continuously vibrating and are warm all over, and the Ch'i flows fluently throughout the entire body. Meanwhile numerous tiny particles are flowing everywhere in the body. "Yishou" (usually putting conscious thought on the Dan Tian) may guide the fire of the heart to descend and the water of the kidneys to ascend in order to maintain a healthful balance of the body's force and improve your health and longevity.

Ch'i Kung is the internal function of conscious thought which is the highest stage of cerebral cortex activity. By practicing Ch'i Kung in a state of complete relaxation and in the tranquility of the natural state, a powerful conscious-ness of vital energy will radiate from the heart, and from this energy will flow a spirit of peace and love. As this ener-gy flows from you to others, it will then also flow outward until it eventually encompasses the cosmos itself.

HOW CH'I KUNG
AFFECTS HEALTH

*My mind is like a pool of water which is so
peaceful when there is no wind . . . .*
— LU YO (POET,
SOUTHERN SUNG DYNASTY)

Those who practice Ch'i Kung enjoy a variety of
health benefits; Ch'i Kung produces many physical,
mental, and emotional effects. All of these effects
contribute to improved overall health, increased longevity,
and the alleviation of pain.

Although Ch'i Kung appears to be primarily a physical
practice, it is necessary that the practitioner work with consciousness or awareness first. It is said that where consciousness goes, the Ch'i follows; thus the practitioner concentrates consciousness where there is pain. This accords

with the theory of traditional Chinese medicine that where there is pain, Ch'i cannot pass through. Ch'i must move freely throughout the body to maintain good health.

Mastery of any of the Ch'i Kung forms (Flying Crane Kung, or Frog Breathing Kung) requires that you learn to control your awareness and focus your consciousness as you perform the movements of the Kung. This will allow you to realize the full benefit of the practice. Controlling your consciousness during Ch'i Kung is called achieving the "Ch'i Kung state."

Practicing Ch'i Kung regularly strengthens your ability to reach the Ch'i Kung state. The Chinese term *yishou* describes the technique used for focusing consciousness. It means thinking about an object, either inside or outside your body. When you concentrate on it and exclude other things from your mind, it is called "sticking to one point, forgetting millions of others." In most of the forms, the yishou location is the Dan Tian, which is the geographic center of the body, three finger-widths below the navel. As Ch'i Kung begins with consciousness, many of the forms begin by focusing consciousness on the yishou location. This can also be called "Ch'i Kung meditation."

Different Ch'i Kung forms, or movements, have effects on different parts of the body. In general, Ch'i Kung improves the operation of various major body systems. Its principal effects are described in the following text.

1 *Ch'i Kung and Weight Loss*

Nowadays obesity has become a serious problem. This kind of disorder may cause many other kinds of diseases, such as hypertension, heart disease, arteriosclerosis, liver problems, waist and leg pain, and so on. People who suffer from obesity are from every age category.

If you suffer from obesity, it is difficult to walk, and this creates problems with all daily activities. Various kinds of medicines and different methods for losing weight are advertised everywhere. It is a pity that the effects of these medicines and therapies for reducing weight only last for a short time. As soon as you stop taking the medicine or therapy you gain back the weight you've lost.

People worry about the harmful side-effects that the weight-loss medicines produce in the body. Therefore, people are longing for a better method for losing weight, one which has neither negative side-effects nor lasts only a short time. If you hope to really lose weight permanently, the best solution is to practice Ch'i Kung.

2 *Practicing Ch'i Kung Intensifies and Regulates Cerebral Activities and Readjusts and Improves the Functioning of the Nervous System*

An average human cerebrum has approximately 14 to 15 billion nerve cells, but only a small fraction of them are normally used (about 1 percent according to American scientists' reports). Medical science attaches great importance to the cerebral cortex, but the deeper cerebral layer is studied less. There is also a lack of understanding of the functions of the frontal lobes of the cerebrum.

When a person reaches the quietest Ch'i Kung state, activities in the cerebral cortex are restrained and slowed down; this allows the cortex to rest. This also allows nerve signals to cross the shallow layers of the cortex and stimulate the deeper layers. Studies have shown that in the Ch'i Kung state, nerve cells in the deeper cerebral layer are excited while the cortex cells are relaxed and passive.

If you are unwell and wish to heal yourself using Ch'i Kung, you must listen quietly to your internal consciousness and then train yourself consciously in accordance with its indications. This internal consciousness can best be felt when the cerebral cortex is most relaxed. When a signal crosses the relaxed cortex and enters the deeper cerebral layer, it stimulates the deeper nerve cells to activity. One purpose of Ch'i Kung is to let the nerve cells in the deeper cerebral layer get excited and become activated so that they can create a stronger electric current in the brain.

Electroencephalogram (EEG) readings have shown that brain function in a Ch'i Kung-trained adult resembles that of a younger person; the brain function of Ch'i Kung-trained youth resembles that of a child. Experiments have also discovered that when elderly and middle-aged people enter the Ch'i Kung state, their EEG readings become stonger and sometimes even similar to young people's.

Ch'i Kung is a useful technique for training and developing the cerebrum. By practicing Ch'i Kung and achieving the Ch'i Kung state, up to 80 percent or 90 percent of the cerebral nerve cells can become activated due to the stimulation of the deeper cerebral nerve cells. This allows the brain to develop a stronger electric current, and this, in turn, allows the practitioner to strengthen the practice of Ch'i Kung meditation.

Cellular activities are stimulated by the body's bioelectric current. When the electric current in the cerebrum and in the central nervous system is strengthened, the bioelectric current in the whole body is stimulated. This, in turn, excites the undeveloped and unused deep-layer cerebral nerve cells and makes you feel as if you've just awakened.

When you start to concentrate your awareness, through the practice of Ch'i Kung, your consciousness of the yishou location begins to release electric currents that are called "Ch'i feelings" in Ch'i Kung. This practice makes the nervous electric current at the yishou location stronger and strengthens the bioelectric current throughout the body, so that cell activity throughout the body is stimulated.

Eighty to 90 percent of the cerebral nerve cells in the body are normally asleep, but when you are in the Ch'i Kung state, all these cells can awaken and begin to work. It is recognized that all body cells have their own energy and functions. The cerebral nerve cells have enormous functional capacity, but ordinary people don't know how to develop and make full use of them, so they waste most of them. Performing Ch'i Kung, by stimulating both nerve-system electric current and bioelectric current, awakens all cells, stimulates them to greater activity, and harmonizes their functions.

One of my students, a young woman from Hong Kong, was troubled by a facial nerve that was extremely painful. After practicing Ch'i Kung for only a few weeks, the nerve stopped bothering her; the combined relaxation and stimulation produced by the practice of Ch'i Kung allowed her nerves to heal themselves and function correctly again.

Ch'i Kung practice also moderates the activity of the sympathetic nervous system that regulates the functioning of the internal organs. The sympathetic nervous system suppresses the activity of the internal organs; performing Ch'i Kung changes its operation so the internal organs can work in accordance with their needs. Because the organs can work continuously when the sympathetic nervous system is suppressed, they can readjust their functioning automatically, both working and resting as needed. This allows the body's overall metabolic rate to be reduced, which, in turn, reduces the body's energy consumption. With energy consumption reduced, the body can begin to restore its energy reserves.

Stimulation of the deeper cerebral cells is also assisted by improved blood flow in the brain, and the slow blood circulation improves when the cerebrum relaxes. This cerebral relaxation is not normally achieved by other means of physical exercise, so the same effect is not achieved even though blood circulation in the body is stimulated by exercise. In fact, ordinary exercise, such as track and field events, makes the cerebrum more tense.

Ch'i Kung meditation and the practice of Ch'i Kung are the key to developing aspects of our nervous systems that are normally wasted. Ch'i Kung promotes relaxation of the shallow cerebral cells, stimulation of the deeper cerebral cells, stimulation of the body's bioelectric and nervous-system currents, moderation of the sympathetic nervous system, and increase in blood flow to the brain. These effects support each other by feedback processes and will help to develop your nervous system so that it can reach its potential.

3 Performing Ch'i Kung Regulates and Improves the Blood Circulation System

Practicing Ch'i Kung keeps the blood vessels elastic. When your heart contracts and pumps blood into your arteries, your blood vessels suddenly expand. When your heart relaxes, your blood vessels contract. Ch'i Kung movements make the blood vessels expand and contract, which keeps them elastic and capable of automatically functioning correctly. By maintaining blood-vessel elasticity, Ch'i Kung can help a person avoid heart disease and strokes. In addition, improved blood-vessel elasticity reduces the amount of work the heart is required to do.

It has been found that when people with high blood pressure enter the Ch'i Kung state, the blood-vessel tension lessens and blood pressure drops. The Shanghai High

Blood Pressure Institute reported, after studying 100 cases, that blood pressure began to drop after 5 minutes of quiet and relaxed meditative sitting. After 20 minutes of Ch'i Kung practice, blood pressure reductions were comparable to reductions caused by medication, and the results lasted for approximately 3 hours. This worked for 97 percent of the patients.

Adequate levels of blood micro-elements also contribute to improved health and longevity, and Ch'i Kung increases the levels of micro-elements in the blood. There are fourteen important blood micro-elements, zinc being the most abundant. Zinc is related to the actions of the 80 kinds of fermentation, which play an important role in our physiology and biochemistry. As a result, adequate levels of zinc in the blood may promote long life. Ch'i Kung training or treatment helps develop higher levels of zinc, and Ch'i Kung practitioners often enjoy greater longevity than others.

At present, heart disease is one of the three most common causes of premature death in humans. According to some scientific studies, it should be possible for humans to live 150 to 200 years, but heart disease and other factors shorten ordinary people's lives to 70 or 80 years. Many elderly people die of heart disease without advance knowledge of it. When a heart attack occurs, the blood supply to part of the heart become inadequate, which causes cells in that part of the heart to die. If this process continues, the heart becomes unable to maintain circulation, and death results.

Ch'i Kung training for the middle-aged and elderly can help prevent premature development of various diseases of the circulatory system, such as blood clot development, strokes, cerebral hemorrhage, and heart disease. It has also been discovered that Ch'i Kung is very effective in reducing the effects of various diseases. For example, although arteriosclerosis and cerebral artery hardening may develop due to aging, practicing Ch'i Kung can help improve the blood-vessel elasticity and change the course of these afflictions.

For some elderly people, difficulty in maintaining a constant body temperature causes them to feel excessively hot in summer and cold in winter. Ch'i Kung training can help them to regain their ability to maintain body temperature by improving blood circulation in their extremities and readjusting slow blood circulation.

Practicing Ch'i Kung affects the circulatory system by changing the way that blood flow is regulated. According to studies, when one enters the Ch'i Kung state, the blood supply begins to change automatically. Ordinarily, people are tense; their muscles are unnecessarily taut and their brains are constantly occupied by a flow of thoughts. The body responds by raising the pulse rate and increasing blood pressure and flow as though it is working. When a person enters the Ch'i Kung state, the body and brain both can relax and the heart and circulatory system respond by resting. Even as the circulatory system is resting from its usual needless tension, the Ch'i Kung movements compress, stretch, and flex the blood vessels.

The inner rest of the Ch'i Kung state is critical in maintaining blood-vessel elasticity, proper blood pressure, and the health of the heart. It allows Ch'i and blood to circulate freely and promote optimum health in all parts of the body. Even in advanced age, when the heart is gradually declining, Ch'i Kung practitioners can regulate and readjust their blood circulation, so they often live longer than other people.

4 Ch'i Kung Practice Regulates the Function of the Respiratory System

When you enter the Ch'i Kung state, the body is able to relax by releasing the unnecessary tensions it ordinarily maintains. As it relaxes, the body reduces its oxygen requirement to that which it needs for the relaxed state. When you practice Ch'i Kung in the relaxed state with a straight back, the lungs are unrestricted. This allows lung pressure to be low during breathing, so the lungs enlarge easily and breathing is comfortable. At the same time, the shoulders and chest can relax while the back is strengthened.

In contrast, running makes the lungs work harder to absorb the greater quantity of oxygen that is required by the activity. The more oxygen the runner absorbs, the more is consumed. Performing Ch'i Kung allows the lungs to collect oxygen more easily and the body to absorb it more efficiently. Thus Ch'i Kung is useful for people with heart disease, lung disease, bronchitis, and asthma, because it helps to regulate the respiratory system.

In addition to breathing and exchanging carbon dioxide for oxygen, the lungs help secrete hormones to produce prostaglandin, which can help prevent feebleness. In general, high levels of prostaglandin improve health. By reducing the demands of unnecessary tension on the lungs and promoting their efficient functioning, Ch'i Kung helps improve the secretion of these hormones.

5 *Practicing Ch'i Kung Improves and Regulates the Digestive System*

Practicing Ch'i Kung improves gastrointestinal activities and automatically reinforces the process of digestion. Some aspects of Ch'i Kung are specifically designed to stimulate the internal organs; as a result, Ch'i Kung can be more effective than other physical exercises. The saliva of Ch'i Kung practitioners contains higher concentrations of various micro-elements that help digestion, than the saliva of other people. In addition, studies have shown that Ch'i Kung increases the production of saliva, gastric juices, and intestinal juices. These juices contain a strong quality of fermentation, and one of the roles of the 80 kinds of fermentation is digestion. By increasing the levels of the micro-elements in the saliva, increasing the production of saliva and other digestive juices, and by strengthening the quality of fermentation of the digestive juices, Ch'i Kung makes the practitioner's digestion much more efficient and effective.

Because of the enrichment of saliva, it is said in China that the saliva of Ch'i Kung practitioners has a natural immunity which helps the body resist oral cavities, gastritis, and enteritis. In addition, its qualities of ferment and starch ferment are intensified and the concentrations of micro-elements are elevated. In Chinese Ch'i Kung, such saliva is called "gold and jade saliva," and is considered very valuable. It is considered to be so beneficial that one should never spit such saliva, but instead should swallow it (with consciousness) to the lower part of the Dan Tian, in the region of the small intestine.

Ch'i Kung also improves the absorbing function of the small intestine. There are two main factors contributing to this. First, the food that reaches the small intestine has already been combined with the enhanced saliva and digestive juices stimulated by Ch'i Kung, and second, the practice of Ch'i Kung itself increases the flow of Ch'i and blood throughout the body and enhances the operation of all the internal organs.

There are two basic rules for living a very long time (over 100 years) while maintaining vigor and good health. The first rule is to eat less food; the second rule is to take less sleep. Less sleep can, when combined with Ch'i Kung, help to make the cerebral cells in the deeper layers of the brain begin to awaken and work. Life is prolonged when the bulk of these cells begin to work, which is the secret of taking less sleep. Eating less food helps to maintain and strengthen the gastric and intestinal functions. The simple principle behind this rule is that digestion consumes energy as well as producing it. Because many people think only of what they like, and not of what they need, they eat too much food and food of the wrong kinds, which stresses the digestive system needlessly. Just as a machine grinding wheat grinds itself, too, our digestion wears itself as it works. Less eating gives rise to less energy consumption and less wear on the digestive system.

6 *Ch'i Kung Practice Can Improve the Function of the Endocrine System*

All men and women have hormones in their bodies, produced and secreted by the various endocrine glands. The internal secretion system is a complicated and important one, linked with growth, health, self-defense, metabolic rate, reproduction, aging, longevity, and many other aspects of our bodily existence. Ch'i Kung helps to balance the functions of the endocrine glands, which harmonizes the body and increases longevity.

Menstruation and menopause are closely related to each other; they are both regulated by ovarian secretions of hormones. Normally, a woman may start to menstruate at 14 and begin menopause around 45. One of my students, a young woman from the Philippines, had not had her period for three-and-a-half months. She was taking medication, which was having no effect, and she was emotionally upset. After two weeks of Ch'i Kung training, her period started again.

Ch'i Kung can play an important role in restoring the secretion of hormones, because Ch'i Kung stimulates and regulates the activities of the endocrine glands. The free flow of Ch'i and blood produced by Ch'i Kung, and the quiet inner state produced by Ch'i Kung meditation both allow the body to adjust itself automatically to reach its optimal inner functioning.

Ch'i Kung is safer and healthier than hormone medications because it can be difficult to find the right dosage of a hormone. The body's need for a particular hormone can change during the day, even in the space of an hour; if there is too much of a hormone, it can be as bad as not enough. Ch'i Kung helps the body to regulate its own hormone secretion automatically in accordance with its needs, which sustains both health and longevity.

7 *Ch'i Kung Regulates and Improves the Functions of Muscles and Bones*

Ch'i Kung exercises the muscles by both contracting and stretching them; practitioners' muscles are kept much more flexible than other people's. Ch'i Kung also keeps the joints limber by flexing them and maintaining their range of movement. By promoting the flow of Ch'i and blood, Ch'i Kung sustains the activity of the blood-producing bone marrow.

As people age, their bones can become brittle and easy to break. Practicing Ch'i Kung can help people maintain muscle tone, joint flexibility, and bone strength as they get older.

8 *Practicing Ch'i Kung Can Help Maintain and Improve the Immune System*

Ch'i Kung has two principle effects that reinforce the action of the immune system: it stimulates and balances the body's overall functioning, and it strengthens the immune system itself. Medicine by itself generally cannot strengthen the immune system.

Practicing Ch'i Kung increases the level of white blood cells in the body and improves their vigor and ability to resist diseases. When this happens, resistance to diseases improves, in particular immunity to the common cold.

9 *Practicing Ch'i Kung Improves the Body's Vitality*

Ch'i is the vital force in all living things. It appears at the instant of the beginning of life, whether it be the life of a plant, an insect, an animal, or a person. When there is greater Ch'i in a living organism, the organism is healthier and more vigorous.

THE BASIC CH'I KUNG METHODS

Where water flows, a channel will be formed.
— CHINESE PROVERB

Y ou might be wondering whether you can really learn Ch'i Kung from a book, without the help of a live teacher. The answer is a qualified "yes." This book is intended to help you start to explore the principles and methods of Ch'i Kung on your own. If you find Ch'i Kung interesting, I recommend that you then look for a qualified teacher to help you.

KNOWING SATISFACTION WILL ALWAYS KEEP ONE HAPPY

He rides on an attractive horse,
  while I ride on an ugly donkey.

Looking forward at him,
*   it seems that I am in an awkward situation.*
When I look backward,
*   I see a man who is pushing a wheelbarrow.*
Comparatively speaking,
when looking forward,
*   I am not as rich as he is,*
but looking backward,
I am riding on a small donkey
*   and I feel very lucky.*

A qualified Ch'i Kung teacher will be able to tell which practices are the most beneficial for you, because each individual has different needs and limitations. Also, if you aren't getting the desired effect, or if you start to encounter difficulties or discomfort, a teacher can determine the problem and correct it. However, if you continue in your practice of Ch'i Kung, this book can be a valuable source of information and guidance.

How can you select a style of Ch'i Kung to practice? Again, a teacher can help in this area, but many of the forms of Ch'i Kung described in this book will help promote good health. Also, these forms are safe to practice on your own. I recommend beginning with the Flying Crane Kung, because it is easy to learn, gives good results quickly, and involves work on consciousness, Ch'i, and movement simultaneously. If you remember the essential principles of Ch'i Kung, you will quickly achieve the best results with the least chance of encountering difficulties:

1 Take one step at a time

Don't be anxious for success. Don't try to rush ahead without really learning the introductory material. Also, don't force yourself; if you stretch too far or overdo it, it is not good for you.

2 Be persistent

Only sufficient regular practice will allow you to develop the skills and produce the effects needed to realize the full benefits of Ch'i Kung.

3 Be relaxed, quiet, and natural

The most important element of Ch'i Kung is to relax and quiet your mind and give it a chance to rest. This alone will relieve stress and improve your health. Moving forms of Ch'i Kung consist primarily of natural movements that are not forced. You must learn to relax all the muscles of your body and move gently without being distracted by either your thoughts or the outside world.

4 Become a combination of movement and stillness

Try to combine the body's smooth and graceful movements with inner stillness.

There are three basic Ch'i Kung methods: Quiet Kung, Active Kung, and Combined Quiet and Active Kung. Quiet Kung consists of meditations or inner practices that are performed without external movement. Active Kung combines disciplined movements of the body with inner mental practices. Combined Quiet and Active Kung involves both moving and non-moving practices.

These basic methods are built upon developing discipline and control in three areas—breath, posture, and the mind. If you learn only the outer movements of the active Kungs described in this book, you will realize only a small fraction of the possible benefit of Ch'i Kung. The following discussion is intended to help you learn the inner practices of Ch'i Kung.

Regulating the Mind

While traveling in the mountains, I came to a tranquil pool of clear water. Several lovely country girls were gazing into the pool at the reflections of their beautiful faces in its mirror-like surface. Your mind is like a pool of water, potentially calm and peaceful, a beautiful place that can be a source of energy and vigor. A pool of water, when it is disturbed all day, becomes muddy and confused. Only when the disturbance is removed can it gradually clear and show its tranquil beauty again.

No matter which form of Ch'i Kung you practice, the most important single aspect is what the Chinese call "the keeping of the mental state." This means that you must try to achieve a tranquil and quiet inner state without any distracting thoughts or desires. To do this, all your awareness must be concentrated on something other than your usual thoughts.

If you achieve this inner concentration, your cerebral cortex will enter a special state which will greatly reduce your responsiveness to external stimuli. The more intensely you can develop this state, the more beneficial your Ch'i Kung practice will be. There are five principal techniques for achieving this state:

1 *Focusing Thought on a Point (Yishou)*

This is the most common technique used with the Active Kung described in this book. To do this, you must concentrate your awareness on a single point in your body (the Yishou location), and hold it there. You must try to avoid all inner distractions and desires; use your focused awareness to keep them away, but don't force it too much. If you lose your attention momentarily, simply bring it back to the point again and continue on.

2 *Silent Reading*

Picture a few simple words in your mind, words that have a positive association, and read them over and over in silence until you achieve a tranquil inner state. The Chinese might contemplate the words *son jin*, which means relaxation and silence. You might try such words as joy, quiet, happy, or relax.

3 Free Breathing

Without guiding or leading the movements, concentrate your awareness on the movements and sensations of your own breath, such as the movement of your chest. Your breathing must be natural and free for you to reach the tranquil state that is the goal.

4 Listening to Your Breath

Focus on the sound of your own breathing. As time passes, if you are able to concentrate, other sounds and distractions will fade and you will reach the desired state. Remember to allow your breathing to be natural and free.

5 Counting Your Breaths

Without guiding or leading your breathing, count each inhalation and exhalation as one breath. This is called "counting xi" (pronounced "she"), because in China, each combined in and out breath is called a xi. At first, count the xi from 1 to 10, then take a break. When you resume, count from 11 up to 100. As you concentrate on counting xi, you will gradually enter the tranquil inner state of Ch'i Kung.

Regulating the Breath

Respiration is the most important part of Ch'i Kung therapy. The breathing movement and the method of breathing, through training consciously and seriously, might be changed from the normal thoracic form into the abdominal form, from shallow to deep breaths; and finally it is to be improved to the Dan Tian (an acupuncture point three fingers' width below the navel) form of breathing. It will extend the lungs' capacity, improve the gas metabolism and blood circulation. And it also plays a part in massaging internal organs so that it helps absorption and digestion. All these changes achieve the purpose of protecting health and strengthening the body, and also increasing the effectiveness of treating and preventing diseases.

There are many kinds of breathing movements, but, in general, the following eight kinds of breathing movements are usually practiced:

1 Natural Breathing

This is the normal form, instinctive breathing without conscious control. It is shallow, smooth, and gentle, but superficial.

2 Favorable Breathing

This is a form of abdominal breathing. When inhaling, the abdomen protrudes (convex ⌐‾⌐). When exhaling, the abdomen contracts (concave [⎍]). This is caused by the diaphragm descending and pushing on the digestive organs during inhalation, but during exhalation, ascending and pushing upward on the lungs. It is practiced to achieve a great amplitude of diaphragmatic movement and gradually develops into an abdominal breathing, that is, breathing with the abdominal wall.

3 Reverse Breathing

When inhaling, the abdomen is concave (contracts [⎍]), it is curved just like any part of the inside of an egg; but when exhaling, the abdomen is curved just like any part of the outside of an egg, that is, the abdomen protrudes (convex [⎍]). This form is just the reverse of that in favorable breathing.

4 Holding Breathing

There are two types of this breathing. One is consciously to prolong the time of inhalation, between inhaling and exhaling, while the other type is to prolong the exhaling duration consciously.

5 The Method of Nasal Inhaling and Oral Exhaling

In normal breathing people inhale and exhale with their noses, but this type of breathing is applied to those people whose nasal or respiratory passages are strictured and obstructed.

6 Method of Ventilation through the Du and Ren Channels

The practitioners adopt reverse breathing to inhale through the nose. At the same time, they must imagine that the Ch'i is directing to and reaching their perineum along the spinal column to the top of the head (Ba Hui point—crown of the head) and exhaled through the nose. It is also called the "Small Cycle Kung of Breathing."

7 Latent Breathing

After one has been thoroughly trained in favorable and reverse breathing, this method of breathing appears naturally. The features are: continuous, tender, even and deep exhaling for each breathing movement. When fingers are put under the practitioner's nostril, there is no sensation of the Ch'i flux at all.

8 Genuine Breathing

This is an advanced state of breathing practice. There is an old proverb: "The respiration of common breathing will stop at last, while that of true breathing moves spontaneously." To stop breathing, we do not mean to stop it with conscious force. This state should be achieved by extreme tranquillity of the mind. The more quiet the mind, the more superficial and slight the breathing will be. Vital energy seems to cease and the mind has stopped. Only a very slight breathing signifies the presence of one's life. Superficially, the practitioner seems to have stopped breathing, but, in fact, he or she is still breathing with his or her navel (umbilicus). Vital energy moves about and pulsates inside the abdomen, and therefore this kind of breathing is also called fetal breathing.

•   •   •

These eight kinds of breathing methods are used to treat different kinds of disease. Favorable Breathing has a better effect on the treatment and prevention of cardiovascular and cerebral-vascular disease. Holding Breathing and Reverse Breathing are better for the treatment and prevention of digestive disorders. Nasal Inhaling and Mouth Inhaling breathing methods are better for the respiratory system, while ventilation through the Du and Ren channel method[3] has good effects on the prevention and treatment of nervous system diseases. It is advisable for students to carefully choose the best method suitable for their real condition and disease.

---

3. *Du Channel*: Belongs to the Yang force. There are 28 acupuncture points in all—from Changch'iang to Mouth-Yinchaio. *Ren Channel*: Belongs to the Yin force. In all, there are 214 acupuncture points—from Ch'engchiang to Huiyn (perineum). See appendix for more information about the Du and Ren channels.

When practicing, if you feel uncomfortable, you must change into natural breathing at once. At the very beginning, practice a few minutes; by and by, when you feel comfortable, then the time of breathing may increase, but 10 to 15 minutes is enough and not too much. You should practice and cultivate your breathing to achieve a natural, smooth, and gentle breathing under the direction of fundamental principles. You must remember not to be over-anxious for quick results and should go step-by-step to achieve deep, smooth, and gentle breathing.

Regulating the Posture

It is necessary to give attention to the correct posture when practicing Ch'i Kung. You must be able to relax your muscles and assume a comfortable position in order to develop proper breathing, and to bring the mind into a relaxed, tranquil, and natural state. In addition, each posture has a different effect on your body and on your Ch'i, so the selection of an appropriate posture will depend on your conditions and needs. Some common Ch'i Kung postures are:

1 *Normal*
Sitting Posture

Select a flat, armless chair that is the right height so you can sit with your feet flat on the floor. Sit straight up on the edge of the chair with your torso and thighs forming a 90-

degree angle. Put your hands on your knees, which should be about a shoulder-width apart. Tuck in your chin, touch the tip of your tongue to the roof of your mouth, applying a slight pressure, and relax your shoulders and chest.

2 Cross-Legged Posture

Sit upright without a back support on a hard, flat surface, such as the floor, and cross your legs naturally, without straining. Let your hands rest in your lap in front of your lower abdomen, close to your body.

3 Supine (lying down) Posture

Lie on your back on a hard or firm, flat surface with a single pillow under your head. Keep your arms and legs straight, with your arms close to your sides, and relax.

4 Reclining (on your side) Posture

Lie on your right side on a hard or firm surface with a single pillow under your head so that your neck is comfortable. Keeping your upper body straight, bend your top leg so that it rests on the bottom leg. Rest your left arm so that the left hand lies on your hip near the buttock, palm down. Bend your right arm so that the right hand lies on the pillow next to your head, palm up.

5 *Standing Posture*

Stand erect, with your knees slightly bent, feet shoulder-width apart, with toes pointing slightly inward. Keep your eyes and mouth gently closed and touch the roof of your mouth with the tip of your tongue. Relax your chest and shoulders, and then bring your hands out in front of you about the height of your solar plexus, with your elbows bent comfortably. Separate and curve your fingers as though your hands are resting on top of a huge ball.

6 *Walking Posture*

Stand quietly for 2 or 3 minutes, then start the walking posture by stepping forward with the left foot. Hold your hands palms down at about the level of your waist, about 6 inches from your body. Moving slowly, let your heel touch the ground first and sway your body and hands to the right. Next, step forward with the right foot as your body and hands sway left. Breathe in through the nose and out through the mouth.

Ch'i Kung, of whichever type, combines work on the mind, breath, and posture. You can practice many of the exercises described above as forms of Quiet Kung to get a taste of the inner state produced by practicing Ch'i Kung. In particular, practice regulating your mind. Remember, start slow and easy, and take one step at a time.

For your Ch'i Kung practice try to select a quiet place where you won't be disturbed. As you practice, you may gradually begin to be able to sense the Ch'i in your body, but even if you can't, you will probably notice that you are beginning to have more energy. When you are ready to move on to the Active Kung, start with the Flying Crane Kung, which is described in the next section.

part two

FLYING CRANE LONGEVITY
KUNG EXERCISES

FLYING CRANE LONGEVITY KUNG

There are many advantages to practicing Flying Crane Longevity Kung.

1. It is easy to learn;

2. It is easy to remember because each movement comes in three parts and follows from left to right and from the top down;

3. It cultivates the union of consciousness, Ch'i, and body movements;

4. It is designed to benefit individual parts of the body by inducing Ch'i movements to those parts;

5. It takes only a short time for some of the beneficial effects to become apparent, although the precise length of time varies from person to person;

6. It is suitable for everyone: young and old, male and female;

7. It easily complements other forms of Ch'i Kung.

The crane is a long-lived bird. It is even-tempered and does not like to quarrel with others. Its movements are tranquil, comfortable, and graceful. By imitating the crane's movements as it lifts its wings or gazes up at the sky, Flying Crane Ch'i Kung develops in us the attributes of the crane: the noble character, the peacefulness, and the calm demeanor.

Flying Crane Kung is well balanced between Active and Quiet Kung, and uses the method of natural breathing. Its slow, graceful movements are performed with a contented and relaxed mind. When practicing, you should dress in loose, comfortable clothing, feeling at ease and smiling inwardly.

There are five parts to Flying Crane Longevity Kung. Each group of exercises can be performed alone, or you can learn them all and do them all at once. It is best to start slowly and enjoy the process of learning.

EXERCISE 1:
ENERGY AND CIRCULATION

This is the basic opening set of exercises. They will help you relieve tension, stimulate circulation, increase energy, and overcome fatigue. They also help you walk better and allow you to free up the ribcage so you can open the meridian pathways in the body.

Looking Over Shoulders

This exercise can help improve the strength of the muscles surrounding the eye sockets, and strengthen the neck muscles to prevent cervico-vertebral ailments. It also stimulates blood circulation in the head to eliminate weariness, dizziness, and other functional disturbances of the central nervous system. It is particularly beneficial to sufferers of hypertension and arteriosclerosis.

FIG. 1   FIG. 2

Starting position: Stand at attention with palms pressed tightly against the thighs.

Slowly turn your head to the left side of your body and look over your left shoulder (fig. 1, 2).

Return to the starting position (fig. 3).

Slowly turn your head to the right side and look over your right shoulder (fig. 4).

Return to starting position. Repeat these movements several times. You may coordinate these movements with respiration: when you turn your head, inhale. When you return to starting position, exhale.

Fig. 3

Fig. 4

Fig. 5

Breathing Ch'i (Vital Energy) from the Universe

Stand with your feet as wide apart as the shoulders, looking straight ahead. Relax from the top of your head to the soles of your feet (fig. 6). Touch the roof of your mouth with the tip of your tongue and calm your mind. Focus your consciousness on the Dan Tian,[1] three finger-widths below your navel, and imagine the Ch'i collecting there.

Fig. 6

---

1. See explanation of Dan Tian in Glossary and Appendix..

FIG. 7

FIG. 8

Draw the Ch'i down through your perineum, up your spine to a point between the shoulders, then down your arms to the Laogongs in the palms of your hands.

Bend your elbows to bring your hands in front of your body, palms facing in and thumbs pointing up (fig. 7). Then hold your arms tight against your body and keep your fingers pointing straight out.

Slowly curl your hands toward your body, leading with your little fingers (fig. 8). Push your hands behind you, keeping the palms facing up (fig. 9 on page 10).

Slightly cupping the hands, swing them forward in an arc until they are straight out in front of you—shoulder high, palms facing up (fig. 10, page 10).

Fig. 9

Fig. 10

Fig. 11

FIG. 12

Bring your arms straight out to your sides, still at shoulder height and with the palms still facing up (fig. 11). Bring your hands over your head and press the palms together (fig. 12).

Interlace your fingers and rotate your hands so that the palms are facing up, away from your head (fig. 13). Your arms should form a circle (fig. 14).

FIG. 13

FIG. 14

FIG. 15

FIG. 16

FIG. 17

Raise your left elbow and let your right elbow and shoulder drop, compressing the ribs together on your right side (fig. 15). Next raise your right elbow and let your left elbow and shoulder drop, compressing the ribs on the left (fig. 16). Repeat this motion 9 times on each side. When you finish, lower your hands slowly to your sides (fig. 17). If you like, you may start by doing this exercise 3 times.

Twisting Legs

Bend your arms in front of your body with the tips of the fingers of both hands opposite each other. Twist your legs toward the left side, the hands also move to the left side

FIG. 18

FIG. 19

FIG. 20

FIG. 21

(fig. 18). Then twist your legs toward the right side, moving hands to the right side also (fig. 19).

Another method: As your arms and hands move to the right side of your body, your legs twist toward the left side (fig. 20). As your arms and hands move to the left side of your body, your legs twist toward the right side (fig. 21). This exercise (or Kung) increases the energy in the body. It makes your legs very strong and is a great help for walking.

Combining the Ch'i of the Universe

In this part of Flying Crane Longevity Kung, Ch'i is drawn into the body from the universe; the meridian pathways are opened, and the Ch'i is mixed and spread throughout the body. You now draw Ch'i in from the heavens through the Laogongs. As you bend left and right in this segment, you stress and relax your ribcage, which lets the Ch'i move freely through it.

Begin with the usual starting posture. Turn your head to the left and point both arms to the left at shoulder level (fig. 22). Your right arm should be bent at the elbow and both

Fig. 22

FIG. 23

FIG. 24

palms should face down. Place the middle fingers of both hands on a straight line (fig. 23).

Using your waist as the axis, rotate your upper body clockwise three times in a big circle. Move smoothly and gently, and very slowly. Let your fingers brush the ground if you can do so without straining (fig. 24). After three full circles, stop with your arms pointing to the left as before, and then make three full circles counter-clockwise. Again, stop with your arms pointing to the left, then let your arms fall slowly to your sides. If your fingers can't brush the ground, do not force it. Only do this as far as you feel comfortable.

Pouring the Ch'i Twice

Begin with the usual starting posture. With both hands, pour the Ch'i into the Tien Mu (the Third Eye in the middle of the forehead) by lifting your arms in front of you as though holding a ball and bringing your Laogongs slowly to your forehead (fig. 25).

Turn your hands palm down as you spread your elbows and expand your chest (fig. 26 on page 60). Pass your hands slowly down the front of your body to guide

Fig. 25

FIG. 26

FIG. 27

Fig. 28

the Ch'i inside you to the Dan Tian. Open your arms as though you were holding a huge ball (fig. 27), and slowly draw your Laogongs to your Dan Tian, pouring the Ch'i into it. When finished, return to the starting posture (fig. 28).

EXERCISE 2:
ROTATING THE NECK, WAIST, AND KNEES

The principle effect of this part of Flying Crane Longevity Kung is to adjust the flow of Ch'i in the Ren Channel and the Du Channel. The Ren Channel runs from the perineum up the front of the body to the lower lip, and belongs to the yin or feminine principle; thus it affects all the yin meridians of the body. The Du Channel runs up the spine from the coccyx to the top of the skull and then to the nose, upper lip, and a point between the gum and the upper lip; it belongs to the yang or masculine principle; thus it affects all the yang meridians of the body. By connecting and balancing these two meridians, all of the meridians of the body will be cleared, and Ch'i will be able to flow freely throughout the body. (See Appendix or Glossary for more information about the Du and Ren Channels.)

Preparation

Stand naturally with your feet parallel. Look straight ahead, touch the roof of your mouth with the tip of your tongue, and relax your body from head to foot (fig. 29). Focus your awareness on your Dan Tian so that the Ch'i will sink there. Move your awareness and your Ch'i through your perineum, up your spine to between your shoulders, and down your arms to the Laogong points in the palms of your hands.

Fig. 29

Eyes and Ears

While keeping your hands on your waist, open your eyes and slowly rotate the eyeballs around the perimeter of the eye socket, in a counterclockwise direction. Repeat this movement three times (fig. 30). Then, keeping the eyes open, rotate them in a clockwise direction (fig. 31). Again, repeat the movement three times. As you become more accustomed to these eye movements you may increase the number of repetitions to nine for each direction. Open your eyes.

FIG. 30   FIG. 31

FIG. 32

FIG. 33

FIG. 34

Move your hands to the top of your ears and place the thumbs at the back of the ears (fig. 32). Press the thumb and the side of the forefinger together, massaging the outer ear as you move your hands down toward the ear-lobes. When you reach the ear-lobes pull them gently as the thumbs and forefingers slip of the ears. Repeat this three times.

FIG. 35

FIG. 36

Massage your neck, using your right hand, with the palm of the hand on your neck. Massage from the left side to the right side. Do this nine times. Then change using the left hand, so that your palm massages your neck softly. Slowly massage your neck nine times (fig. 34).

Bend your arms at the elbows to bring your hands

FIG. 37

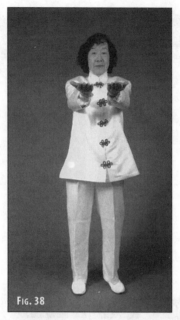

Fig. 38

Fig. 39

FIG. 40

FIG. 41

in front of you, palms facing in and thumbs pointing up (fig. 35, page 67). Leading with the little fingers, curl your hands inward (fig. 36) past your body, and push them behind you, palms back (fig. 37).

Slightly cupping the hands, circle them forward with palms up (fig. 38), ending with arms straight and held full length out in front of the body, at shoulder height.

Separate the arms out to both sides (fig. 39), then move them up over the top of the head, with the palms pressing together (fig. 40).

Bring the palms down in front of the breast bone, palms are opposite each other (fig. 41).

FIG. 42

FIG. 43

Continue to bring the hands down toward the navel (fig. 42) and allow them to separate as you move them to place them on your waist (fig. 43).

Stretching the Neck

This comprises three neck stretches. Each one rotates the neck about a different axis.

1. Stretch the neck forward with the tip of the chin out (fig. 44), so that it draws an arc downward (fig. 45), and then pull it back. Repeat this movement three times.

FIG. 44   FIG. 45

The chin is drawn downward (fig. 46, page 72), then up (fig. 47), making a circle from bottom to top. Repeat this movement in the opposite direction three times.

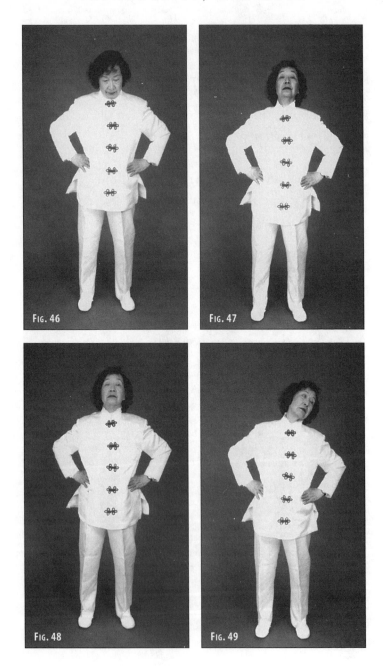

Fig. 46

Fig. 47

Fig. 48

Fig. 49

FIG. 50

2. Now return to the original position, relax the neck, drop the head backward (fig. 48). Rotate the head very slowly, first to the right and forward (clockwise) until the head is fully dropped forward, and then to the left and backward (fig. 49). Continue the movement until you have completed three full rotations. Then reverse the direction, dropping the head backward and then to the left, then forward and on to the right (fig. 50). Continue until you have completed three full rotations.

Rotating the Waist

With the fingers pointed downward (fig. 51), move the hands around the body, along the Daimai. Thumbs are together, joining again at the rear of the body (fig. 52). Palms are now facing outward, thumbs joining one another side by side while held forward of the forefingers, the back of the palms nestled up against the *Shenshu*. The Shenshu are acupuncture points on the back.

With your hands over your kidneys, rotate your waist and thighs clockwise three times. Keep your knees slightly

FIG. 51   FIG. 52

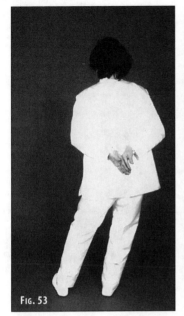

FIG. 53

FIG. 54

bent and look straight ahead; most of the movement must come from your waist and legs. Next, circle counter-clockwise three times.

With your hands still on the kidneys. rotate your waist and thighs in a circle again, from left to right three times (fig. 53).

Then rotate your waist and thighs from right to left three times. Keep your upper torso and shoulders as still as possible and your head looking straight ahead (fig. 54).

FIG. 55

FIG. 56

FIG. 57

Stand with feet parallel as wide as your shoulders (fig. 55). Place your arms in front of your chest with the tips of the fingers of both hands opposite each other, palms facing downward (fig. 56). Look ahead. Slowly squat with torso erect (fig. 57). Stand and slowly squat three times.

EXERCISE 3:
LINKING UPPER AND LOWER BODY CH'I

For this series of exercises be conscious of the Laogongs in the palms of your hands, and of the Dashui, an acupuncture point on the spine at the top of the shoulders. During this movement, inhale the Ch'i from Heaven (Yang) through your Laogongs. The Ch'i in your body can move upward toward the Dazhui.

During the rising and falling movement, pay attention to two other acupuncture points—the Yongquans and the Mingmen. There is a Yongquan point on the sole of each foot, in the hollow formed just behind the ball when you flex each foot backward. The Mingmen is a point on the spine just below the center of the small of your back, under the second lumbar vertebra. When the Mingmen point relaxes, all the principle meridians open, allowing an abundant flow of Ch'i and blood throughout the body. The Yongquan points will connect you with Earth and permit you to inhale the Yin Ch'i as you rise and fall.

Heels and Toes Touch the Ground

Alternate lifting your toes and heels off the ground. As you lift your heels off the ground, the toes touch the ground (fig. 58); as you lift your toes off the ground, the heels touch the ground (fig. 59). Practice this exercise any time, indoors or outdoors. It is very beneficial to your health and, above all, increases the energy of your legs and thighs.

> When a tree begins begins to decay, first of all,
> its roots rot.
> When a person begins to get old, first of all,
> the feet lose strength.
> — CHINESE PROVERB

FIG. 58   FIG. 59

Flying Crane Touching Water

The aim of "Flying Crane Touching Water" is to relax the shoulders, elbows, wrists, legs, knees, and ankles so that the Ch'i and blood of the upper and lower parts of the body will flow freely. The shoulders are used to draw back and push the arms outward. The waist is used to shake the whole body up and down, touching the water. Here the acupuncture points Dazhui and Laogongs play important roles.

The main acupuncture points used in this exercise are the Mingmen and the Yongquan. The major meridian pathways of the whole body will not open unless, first of all, the acupuncture point of the Mingmen relaxes. The Ch'i of the upper and lower parts of the body can link as a whole in order to make the Ch'i and the blood flow easily. Yongquan will connect the Ch'i of the outside with the movements of touching the surface of water up and down. "Inhale Tien (Heaven) Yang to replenish the Ch'i in the body; inhale Di (Earth) Yin to replenish the blood in the body." Thus Yang and Yin balance. Ch'i and blood adjust. The connection of Heaven, Earth, and person as a whole will play the role of adjusting and replenishing the Ch'i and blood.

Preparation

Stand with your feet parallel, shoulder width apart, with your hands hanging naturally at your sides (fig. 60). The tip of the tongue should be touching the hard palate. Smile as if not smiling, look ahead, thinking nothing, and relax from the top of your head to the bottom of your feet. Sink the Ch'i downward to your Dan Tian and begin to concentrate your consciousness on Dan Tian.

Fig. 60

FIG. 61

FIG. 62

Conduct the Ch'i from Dan Tian so it can pass through Huiyin. It travels along Dumai up to the shoulders, then from the shoulders along the arms down to the Laogongs in the palms of the hands. Hold both hands and hold the Ch'i (mentally) as if it were a big ball (fig. 61). Slowly raise up the Ch'i and pour it (mentally) into the Tianmu (forehead, the Third Eye, fig. 62). Then extend your elbows outward, stretching the chest, your palms facing down, so that you slowly conduct the Ch'i from the front of your chest down toward the Dan Tian. You are making the motions *outside* the body but guiding the Ch'i *inside* (mentally) down to the Dan Tian.

Fig. 63

Fig. 64

Shift your weight to the right leg and extend your arms forward, with palms down, wrists loose, and slowly raise your arms (as though fanning a flame). At the same time, raise your left leg, and let the leg hang naturally with toes down (fig. 63). When your arms reach a little above your shoulders, sink from the waist and bring your arms and foot down simultaneously. The ball of your left foot lightly touches the ground as though "touching water." Repeat three times. The consciousness is on the Yongquan (in the soles of the feet) and Laogongs. This motion is like a crane flapping wings and raising its legs; the motion is initiated at the breastbone.

FIG. 65

Then step the crane step: Raise both arms and your left leg. Bring your hands together with the backs of your hands facing each other, and step forward (fig. 64). It seems that you are taking a long step, but, in fact, you draw back your left leg about two or three inches before your right foot.

Now extend both arms outward from the shoulders (fig. 65), turning the fingers into "arrow fingers." The right foot is now raised slightly off the ground, toes hanging downward.

Arms are now drawn back and pushed outward alternately at the shoulders—first the left and then the right—

FIG. 66

FIG. 67

Fig. 68

forming the shape of the dragon undulating (figs. 66, 67 on page 86).

Repeat this exercise three times on each side.

Now release the "arrow fingers," palms still face down. Raise and lower your arms, the waist, and the right foot. Toes face downward, lightly touching the ground as though touching water, in the fashion of a bird alighting from flight (fig. 68). Repeat three times. Consciousness is on the centers of the palms and the center of the sole of the right foot (Yonquan).

Allow your arms to fall slowly and naturally to the sides of the body (fig. 69, page 88). Then, palms down, slowly raise and lower them, along with the waist and right leg, toes pointed downward, lightly "touching the water" three

Fig. 69

Fig. 70

Fig. 71

Fig. 72

times (fig. 70), as previously, but now the hands and foot are in front of the body. Consciousness is on the Yongquan of the right foot and on the Laogongs. The "waist" movement is really attached to the diaphragm, and moves up and down as the diaphragm contracts and expands with your breathing.

Step the crane step. Raise your arms and right leg, and bring your hands together with the backs of your hands facing each other. Step forward (fig. 71).

The left foot is now raised slightly off the ground, the sole of the left foot facing the rear, toes downward (fig. 72). Once again, holding the fingers in the arrow formation, make the motion of the undulating dragon with your arms,

FIG. 73

FIG. 74

alternately drawing back at the shoulder first the left and then the right arm. Repeat three times. Then turning the arrow fingers into Yin palms (palms facing down), raise and lower your arms and waist and left foot. The toes and ball of the left foot should be lightly touching the ground as you come down, three times, like a bird alighting from flight. Consciousness is on the left Yongquan and the Laogongs.

Now your hands hold the Ch'i as though you were holding a ball. Slowly raise up the Ch'i and pour it into the Tianmu (fig. 73). Then, extending the elbows and stretching

FIG. 75

FIG. 76

the chest, palms facing down, slowly conduct the Ch'i from the front of the chest to the Dan Tian (hands on the outside, Ch'i on the inside). Separate your hands, and move them outward and forward in an arc (fig. 74) in front of the body and draw them in to pour the Ch'i into the Dan Tian (fig. 75). Return to the beginning posture (fig. 76).

EXERCISE 4:
REJUVENATING THE
INTERNAL ORGANS

The Flying Crane Longevity Kung is a moving Kung in five parts, each of which has its own action on both the body and the Ch'i. While practicing Exercise 4, try to imitate the crane, the bird of long life. The crane has an even temper and is not quarrelsome; its movements are peaceful and graceful.

In this part of the Flying Crane Longevity Kung, you inhale and exhale Ch'i from the universe around you through your Laogongs, which are points in the center of your palms. You can find this point by curling your middle finger until its tip just touches your palm; try to keep your palm flat (see diagram 1, page 94). The point where your finger touches is the Laogong. Ch'i is inhaled and exhaled through the Laogongs.

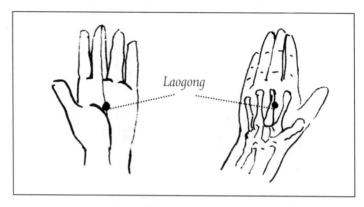

Diagram 1. Laogong. This point is in the center of the palm.
It is a very important point in the treatment of diseases.

While doing this part of Flying Crane Longevity Kung, you connect all the internal organs with Ch'i and rejuvenate them. At the same time, you are moving Ch'i through all the external joints to maintain their flexibility.

Preparation

Stand with your arms at your sides, your feet shoulder-width apart, and toes pointing forward (fig. 77). Touch the tip of your tongue to the roof of your mouth. Breathe naturally, and, looking straight ahead, begin to relax, starting at the top of your head and working down to your feet.

Next, calm and quiet your mind. Focus your consciousness on your Dan Tian (three finger-widths below your navel), which will cause your Ch'i to accumulate there.

FIG. 77

Lifting Your Wings

Move your awareness and Ch'i down to the perineum (the Huiyin) and then up your spinal column (the Du Channel) to a point between your shoulders, and then down your arms to the Laogongs in the center of your palms. Maintain your awareness of the Laogongs and the Ch'i that has been drawn there. Slowly raise your arms to shoulder level in front of you, palms down (fig. 78, page 96).

Bend your wrists backward until your fingers are pointing straight up; flex your fingers backward so that the palms of your hands are convex (fig. 79).

Fig. 78

Fig. 79

Fig. 80

Flatten your hands as you draw them slowly backward toward your head. Bring your hands back past your ears and then push them forward again with the palms forward (fig. 80). Repeat this drawing and pushing motion three times. As you draw your hands back, breathe in the Ch'i from the universe through your Laogongs, and as you push your hands forward, exhale it through your Laogongs back into the universe.

Stretching Your Wings

With your hands flat, move your arms at shoulder height straight out to your sides (fig. 81).

FIG. 81

FIG. 82

FIG. 83

FIG. 84

Bend your wrists to point your fingers straight up; again, the fingers should be flexed backward so that the palms are convex (fig. 82).

Flatten your hands and draw your hands slowly and gently toward your ears, leading with your wrists (fig. 83). After drawing your hands in, push them out sideways, palms first (fig. 84). Repeat this motion three times, each time inhaling and exhaling Ch'i through your Laogongs.

Closing Your Wings

Relax your shoulders and lower your arms to form an angle of about 20 degrees with your torso.

Turn your palms back and push your arms back to about a 45-degree angle, like a crane closing its wings. This draws Ch'i from the universe behind you in through your Laogongs (fig. 85).

Fig. 85

Folding Up Your Wings

Curl your fingers and wrists toward your body and bring your hands up through your armpits, leading with your little fingers.

Bring your hands in front of you, palms up and fingers still curled, to form two paws (fig. 86); your forearms should approximately parallel the ground. As you assume this posture, bend your knees.

Cast off the negative Ch'i through your fingers while keeping the vital Ch'i in your Laogongs (fig. 87).

FIG. 86

FIG. 87

Lift the Ch'i and Pour It into the Crown of Your Head (the Baihui)

Hold the Ch'i as though you are holding a ball, and relax your hands as you lift them in front of you. Raise them over your head and flatten them as you slowly lower them to the crown of your head (fig. 88). Imagine yourself pouring Ch'i into the Baihui, an acupuncture point at the crown of your head.

Fig. 88

Receive Ch'i from Heaven

Interlace your fingers and turn your palms upward. Push your hands up as you inhale the Ch'i from Heaven through the Laogongs (fig. 89). Heaven belongs to the Yang or male principle, as does Ch'i, so this will replenish Ch'i in your body.

Lower your hands to just above your head as you turn them palms down. Keep the fingers interlaced. Letting your hands move to the left, but keeping them raised, move your left elbow forward and down, back, and then return it to its original position (fig. 90).

Fig. 89

Fig. 90

FIG. 91

FIG. 92

Repeat this motion to the right (fig. 91); move your right elbow forward and down, back, and then return it to its original position.

Turn your palms up and push your hands up while stretching your neck vertebrae upward (fig. 92). Repeat the elbow movements to the left and right.

Turn your palms upward and push your hands up again. This time, stretch your sternum and the vertebrae in the middle of your back upward.

Repeat the elbow movements left and right.

Repeat the stretching movement once more. This time, as you push your hands up, bend your knees slightly. Stretch your waist (diaphragm) vertebrae as you breathe in the Ch'i from Heaven through your Laogongs.

Touch the Earth and Inhale the Ch'i

Because the Earth belongs to Yin, this will rejuvenate your blood, which also belongs to Yin. Earlier, you breathed in Ch'i from Heaven (which is Yang). If the Yin and Yang in your body balance, your Ch'i and blood will automatically adjust to the ideal state.

Move your feet slightly so that your toes are parallel. Keeping your fingers intertwined and your palms turned out, slowly bend from the waist until the palms of your hands touch the ground (or as close as you can come) (fig. 93). First touch the ground between your feet.

FIG. 93

Fig. 94

Fig. 95

Fig. 96

Fig. 97

Moving slowly, touch the ground by your left foot (fig. 94), and then by your right (fig. 95). Inhale the Ch'i from Earth through your Laogongs.

Unlace your fingers and bring your right hand over your left as though you are holding a ball (fig. 96). Slowly straighten your body as you do this, keeping your weight on your left leg.

Turning to the left, lift your left leg, heel first, and then replace it heel first so that the toe is pointed out. Raise your left arm as your right hand turns palm up by your waist (fig. 97). Look at the palm of your left hand (the Laogong point) as you bring it slightly above eye level.

Turn your face forward and lift your left hand over your ear, palm down, to pour the Ch'i into the Dan Tian (fig. 98).

FIG. 98

Fig. 99

Fig. 100

Fig. 101

Fig. 102

Slowly lower your hand past your ear (pass your thumb behind your ear) and down the front of your body to your waist. This will guide the Ch'i inside the body to the Dan Tian.

Draw a small flat circle to the left with your left hand (fig. 99). As you move your hand to the left, shift your weight onto your left foot and turn your left hand palm up. As you bring your hand back to your body, turn your body to the right and twist your left foot to the front, turning it on its heel.

Turning to the right, take a small step with your right foot to turn it outward and raise your right hand while looking at its palm (fig. 100).

FIG. 103

FIG. 104

Turn your face forward, pour the Ch'i into your Baihui with your right hand, and lower your right hand past your ear and down the front of your body (fig. 101, page 108).

Take a small step with your right foot to bring your feet parallel and your body facing straight forward. At the same time, form a circle in front of the body with both hands as if holding a very large ball (fig. 102, page 109).

Slowly pull your hands in toward your Dan Tian and pour the Ch'i into it (fig. 103). When finished, return to the beginning posture (fig. 104).

EXERCISE 5:
TOTAL RELAXATION

This part arouses the Ch'i of the whole body to open and close. When you practice, you must pay rapt attention. Inwardly you should be quiet, and outwardly you should have a mild appearance. The mind is without desire, thinking nothing, but your appearance should be calm and elegant. Once you have finished these exercises you will find you have a lot of energy, your mind will be very clear and relaxed, and you will want to do these exercises frequently.

Palms Opening and Closing

Begin with your feet parallel and shoulder width apart. Relax from the top of your head to the bottom of your feet. Smile as if not smiling, to show that your inward mind is happy. The tip of the tongue touches the hard palate. Think

FIG. 105

FIG. 106

FIG. 107

nothing. Look straight ahead and sink the Ch'i to the Dan Tian (fig. 105).

Raise your arms up to shoulder-level height, with the palms upward (fig. 106). Bring them together above your head (fig. 107).

Lower your "He Shi" palms (pressing the palms together) to waist height (fig. 108). Slowly separate your palms (fig. 109). Then bring them together. Repeat this movement three times.

Next raise your "He Shi" palms until the fingers are just under your nose (fig. 110, on page 114).

Open and close your hands (fig. 111), and repeat this movement three times.

Fig. 108

Fig. 109

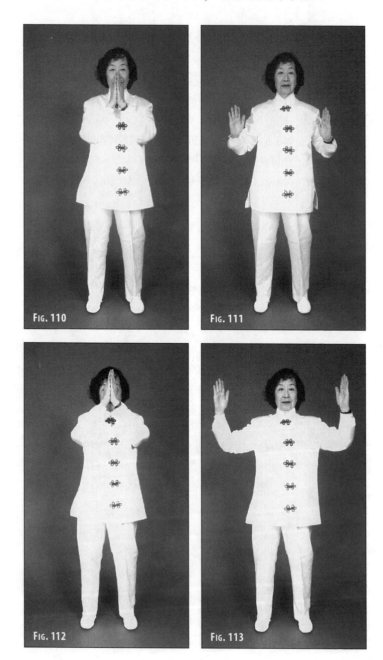

Fig. 110

Fig. 111

Fig. 112

Fig. 113

Now raise your hands up so that your fingertips are level with your eyebrows. Then separate your palms and slowly bring them together (He Shi). Do this three times.

The fourth time raise the palms so that the tip of your fingers are even with the top of your head (fig. 112). Separate and close your palms (fig. 113), and repeat this movement three times.

The fifth time you bring your hands together above your head (fig. 114), open and close your hands, palms facing each other (fig. 115). Repeat this movement three times.

Slowly lower your palms to your waist (fig. 116, on page 116). Separate both hands and make a circular movement from each side (fig. 117).

FIG. 114   FIG. 115

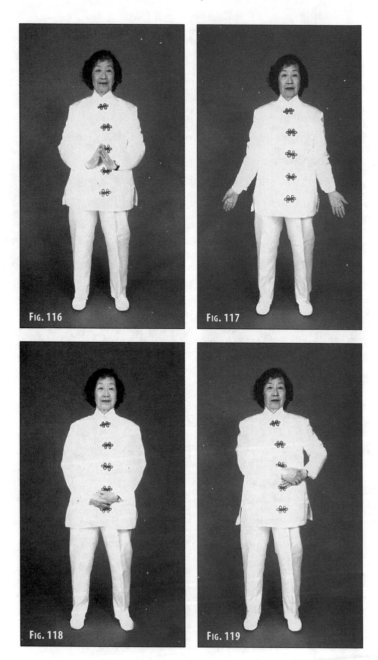

FIG. 116

FIG. 117

FIG. 118

FIG. 119

Fig. 120

Fig. 121

You will next place both hands on the Lower Dan Tian; the right hand should be on the back of the left hand (fig. 118).

Rotate both your hands on the Dan Tian first from the left to the right (fig. 119). Repeat this three times. Imagine the Ch'i circling inside as you do this.

Then rotate them from the right to the left three times (fig. 120). Imagine the Ch'i circling inside as you do this.

Slowly lower your hands and separate them (fig. 121). With both hands, hold the Ch'i and bring it up to pour into the Tianmu (fig. 122, page 118).

Once again hold the Ch'i (fig. 123) and pour it into the Dan Tian (fig. 124) Return to the beginning posture (fig. 125).

FIG. 122

FIG. 123

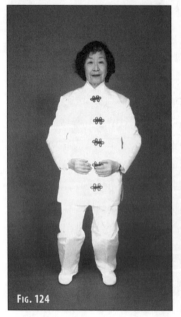

FIG. 124

FIG. 125

BIEN CHIU AND
THE GENERAL

Bien Chiu was a very famous Ch'i Kung Master of ancient times. He was also a well-respected doctor. He lived in the county of Pu Hai, and was the friend of Chi Wang Gong, a general who was renowned for his bravery.

One day Bien Chiu went to visit Chi Wang Gong; when he entered the reception room, he looked at the general for a few moments and said, "You have a sickness in your skin. If you let me help you, I can easily cure it. Otherwise, it's likely to get worse."

Chi Wang Gong said, "Nonsense, I'm not sick; I never get sick," and sent him away because he was irritated by Bien Chiu's claim.

Five days later, Bien Chiu returned for another visit. When he saw Chi Wang Gong, he said, "Lord, you have an illness in your blood, and if you don't let me cure it, surely it will get worse."

Chi Wang Gong was indignant. He said, "I am perfectly healthy. I don't know why you come here and say these things. I am not sick; now go away."

Another five days passed before Bien Chiu returned to see his friend. After looking at him, he said at once, "Lord, your illness has passed into your internal organs and is very serious. I can still cure it if you will let me."

This time, Chi Wang Gong was angry. He stood up, put his hands on his hips and almost yelled, "I thought you were my friend, but you just come here to scare me. There's nothing wrong with me." At once he ordered his attendants to send Bien Chiu out.

When Bien Chiu returned to visit five days later, he entered Chi Wang Gong's room, looked at him carefully, turned around, and left without speaking a word. Chi Wang Gong was shocked. He sent his attendants after Bien Chiu.

When they brought him back, Chi Wang Gong asked, "Why did you look at me that way and then leave without saying anything?"

Bien Chiu answered, "The first time I came to see you, your illness was on the skin and I could easily have cured it with heating pads. The next time I came, the illness was in your blood, but I could still have cured it with acupuncture therapy. When the illness had moved into your internal organs, it would have been harder to cure, but I could have done it with herbal medicines. Now, however, your illness is in the marrow of your bones, and there is nothing I can do."

Chi Wang Gong didn't believe him. "You're crazy! I'm as healthy as a horse." He sent Bien Chiu away.

That night, Chi Wang Gong fell ill, and he couldn't leave his bed until the next morning. He sent his attendants out to find Bien Chiu and bring him back. He finally believed that he was ill and wanted Bien Chiu's help. Although they looked everywhere, they couldn't find him. Five days later, Chi Wang Gong died.

THE SNAKE IN THE CUP

The famous doctor and Ch'i Kung Master of ancient China, Bien Chiu, practiced medicine in the county of Pu Hai. On the inside of his front door hung a beautiful picture of a snake, and across the room on another wall hung a large, ornate mirror.

One day a friend of his visited, and, as is the custom in China, Bien Chiu invited him to share a meal. They talked and ate and drank white wine in Bien Chiu's best crystal glasses.

Bien Chiu's friend seemed a little unhappy when he left, but Bien Chiu didn't think anything of it at the time. However, his friend didn't come back for another visit for a long time. When Bien Chiu went to visit him, it seemed as though his friend was avoiding him.

Before long, other friends told him it was true: his friend was avoiding him. What was more, Bien Chiu heard that his friend was sick. His friend believed he had drunk a snake into his stomach at Bien Chiu's house. Ever since, he feared that the snake was growing larger day by day and if he ate, the snake would eat, too, and get even bigger. The result was that he didn't eat enough and was wasting away from fear and lack of food.

Bien Chu decided he had to help his friend. Through his Ch'i Kung studies, he understood psychology, its effect on health, and how to help cure psychological problems. After some thought, he formed a plan.

Bien Chiu was able to persuade his friend to come visit once more and take a light meal. He carefully arranged everything in his front room exactly as it had been on the day his friend had visited before.

When his friend arrived, Bien Chiu seated him in the same place he had occupied during his previous visit. They ate the meal together, but his friend was silent through most of it, and obviously didn't relish his food. Near the end of the meal, Bien Chiu served a clear white wine in his best crystal glasses.

As his friend lifted his glass to his lips, he started and cried out, "There's a big snake in my cup—I can't drink this kind of wine. What are you trying to do, Bien Chiu?"

Bien Chiu pointed silently to the picture of the snake on one wall, then to the mirror on the wall across from his friend. His friend held up his glass again and saw that the snake in his cup was a reflection of the picture cast onto the bottom of his glass by the mirror.

Bien Chiu calmed his friend. "In your body, there is no snake. The snake is in my picture."

His friend's mind cleared and afterward he began to recover his health, eating enough and visiting his friend, Bien Chiu.

GLOSSARY

ARROW FINGERS: Forefinger (or index finger) and middle finger (or long finger) straight out, with your thumb holding your last two fingers (ring-finger and little finger) over your palm.

BAIHUI: The crown of the head, or above the posterior hairline midway on a line connecting the apexes of the two auricles (both ears).

CHANGQIANG: Midway between the tip of the coccyx and the anus.

CHENGJIANG: In the depression in the center of the mentolabial groove.

CHENGSHAN: The acupuncture point located on the back of each calf. Benefits: it can help to cure lower back pain, constipation, spasm of the large calf muscle, and hemorrhoids.

CHIHU: Below the middle point of clavicle, on the chest.

DAIMAI: Belt Channel, waistline; begins under the navel, where it divides into two branches which extend around the waist to the small of the back (directly below the free end of the eleventh rib, level with the umbilicus).

DAN TIAN: Below the navel one inch, or below navel three finger widths. Actually there are three Dan Tian locations. The Upper Dan Tian is located on the forehead and crown of the head. The Middle Dan Tian is located near the solar plexus. The Lower Dan Tian is located below the navel, and it is to this energy spot that we refer throughout this and all my other books.

DAZHUI: Between the spinous processes of the 7th cervical vertebra and the 1st thoracic vertebra, at the level of the shoulder.

DI: Means Earth, which belongs to Yin.

DUMAI (DU CHANNEL): The Du Channel originates from the inside of the lower abdomen. Descending, it emerges at the perineum. Then it ascends along the interior of the spinal column to Fenfu at the nape, where it enters the brain. It further ascends to the crown and winds along the forehead to the nose. There are 28 points in this channel—and most of them in the back.

EMPTY FISTS: Fingers naturally close together with the thumb touching the tip of the middle (long) finger. Palms are empty.

FENFU: Directly below the external occipital protuberance in the depression between trapezius on both sides.

HE SHI: Pressing palms together.

HUANTIAO: This acupuncture point is located on both buttocks. Indications: pain in the lower back and hip region, pain and weakness of the lower extremities, and hemiplegia (paralysis of one side of the body).

HUIYIN: In the center of the perineum. It is between the anus and scrotum in males and between the anus and posterior labial commissure in females.

JINGMEN: On the lateral side of the abdomen, on the lower border of the free end of the twelfth rib.

JOYU: The region of the kidneys.

LAOGONG: The point near the center of the palm (Inside Laogong); Outside Laogong is located in the center of the back of the hand. *Lao* equals "work, labor"; *Gong* equals "palace." This point is very important in the treatment of diseases. Location: At the point where the tip of the middle finger touches the palm when you close your fist.

LU GE: *Lu* means "six," *Ge* means "connecting together," six joints: shoulder, elbow, wrist, thigh, knee, and ankle. There are also six directions in nature: east, west, south, north, up (Heaven or sky), down (Earth or ground). These are outside our bodies, but inside the body we have heart, liver, spleen, lungs, kidneys, and stomach.

MINGMEN: The point on the lower back, opposite the navel (below the spinous process of the 2nd lumbar vertebra).

MOUTH-YINGJIAO: Between the upper lip and the upper labial gingiva in the frenulum of the upper lip.

PERINEUM: The area between the anus and the posterior part of the external genitalia, especially in females.

REN CHANNEL: The Ren Channel arises from the lower abdomen and emerges from the perineum. It runs in front of the pubic region and ascends along the interior of the abdomen, passing through Quanyuan and the other points along the front midline to the throat. Running further upward, it curves around the lips, passes through the cheek and enters the area beneath the eye socket. The points of this channel are 24 in number.

SANYINJIAO: The meeting point of the three yin channels of the foot (the Spleen Channel of Foot—Taiyin; the Kidney Channel of Foot—Shaoying; and the Liver Channel of Foot—Jueyin).

SHENZHU: Below the spinous process of the 3rd thoracic vertebra.

SHENYU: These two points are located on both sides of the Mingmen. They store water for the proper functioning of the kidneys.

Shuan Hui Ch'i: Both hands hold the Ch'i of the universe and pour it into Tienmu or Dan Tian.

TIEN: Means "Heaven," which belongs to Yang.

TIENMU: Forehead, part of face above eyebrows between temples.

TUNG KUNG: Moving Kung.

YAMEN: At the middle point of the nape of the neck.

YINGTAN: The point located above and between the eyebrows. This is where Ch'i enters the head to benefit the brain.

YONGQUAN: In the depression appearing on the sole when the foot is flexed, toes curled downward, approximately at the junction of the front and middle third of the sole.

ZANZHU: On the medial extremity of the eyebrow, or on the notch at the top of the eye socket.

ZHANGMEN: On the lateral side of the abdomen, below the free and the 11th floating rib.

appendix

ACUPUNCTURE POINTS
AND ENERGY CHANNELS

Places to focus consciousness
Places where energy is received from the Universe

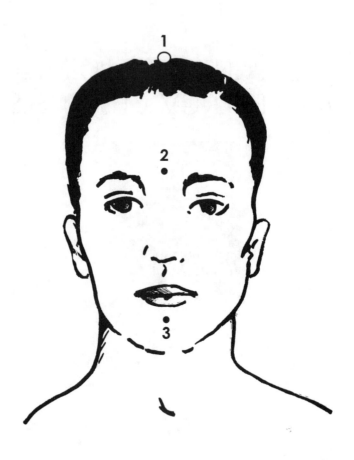

1
Baihui

Bai (*hundred, all*), Hui (*meet*)
This point is at the top of the head. All parts of the body and all meridians pay respect to it.

2
Tianmu

Tian (*sky, heaven*), Mu (*eyes*)
This is the forehead point, just below the center of the forehead. Also referred to as the "Third Eye," point of clarity.

3
Chengjiang

Cheng (*receive*), Jiang (*saliva*)
This point is in the middle of the depression between the lower lip and the chin. Saliva collects at this point.

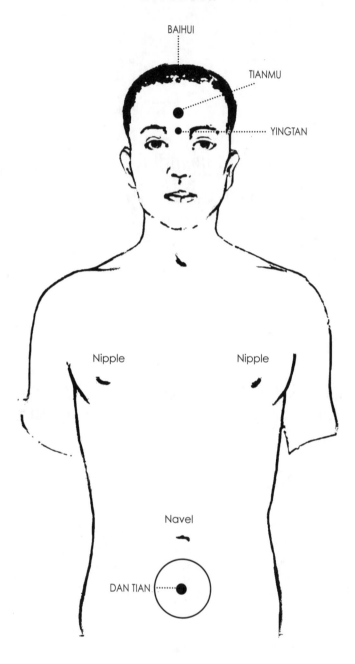

BAIHUI

TIANMU

YINGTAN

Nipple

Nipple

Navel

DAN TIAN

Dan Tian and the
Major Acupuncture Points

In descending order from the top of the skull:

Baihui: At the top of the head; crown.

Tianmu: Between the eyebrows, just below the center of the forehead. The "Third Eye."

Yingtan: Between the eyebrows.

Dan Tian: The point three fingers width below the navel. This point can be called the "sea" for the Ch'i of the whole body.

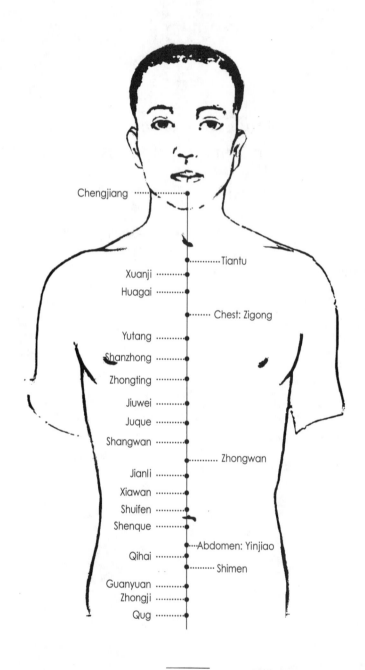

Chengjiang

Tiantu

Xuanji

Huagai

Chest: Zigong

Yutang

Shanzhong

Zhongting

Jiuwei

Juque

Shangwan

Zhongwan

Jianli

Xiawan

Shuifen

Shenque

Abdomen: Yinjiao

Qihai

Shimen

Guanyuan

Zhongji

Qug

Ren Mai (Ren Channel)

The Ren Channel arises from the lower abdomen and emerges from the perineum. It ascends along the interior of the abdomen, and the front midline to the throat, up to the Chengjiang. The Ren Channel has 24 points.

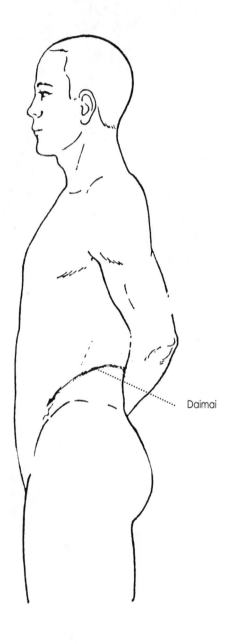

Daimai

Daimai

This is the line or meridian that circles the waist. "Holy Wheel Rotating Forever" dredges into the channel of Dai Mai.

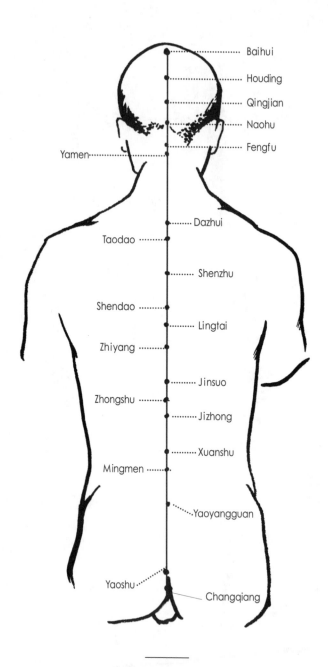

Du Mai (Du Channel)

This is a channel that begins at Changqiang. This channel is very strong, connecting the nervous system of the body. It passes through 28 acupuncture points located mostly along the spine. At the nape of the neck (or back), this channel enters the brain, moving through Baihui, around on the forehead and ending at a point at the front of the hard palate (roof of the mouth).

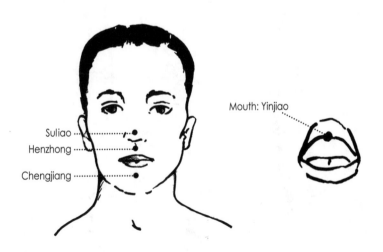

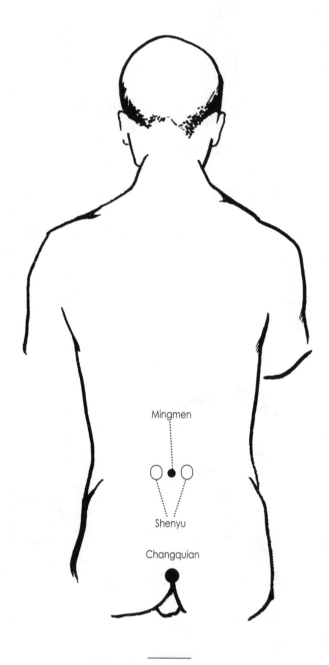

Mingmen

Shenyu

Changquian

Mingmen

This point is in the lower back opposite the navel. This is a very important point through which the vital energy of life goes in and out; it is a gate.

Shenyu

These two points are located on each side of the Mingmen. These points store up water for the proper functioning of the kidneys.

Changquian

This point is located on the coccyx or tail bone (the last bone of the spine). This point is the starting point of the Du Channel. It can be used to strengthen Yang energy of the kidney and therefore treats premature ejaculation and impotence.

Huantiao

This acupuncture point is located on both buttocks. Indications: pain in the lower back and hip region, pain and weakness of the lower extremities and hemiplegia.

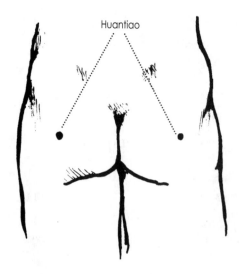

Huantiao

Huiyin

This point is at the lowest part of the abdomen. It is a place where Yin energy gathers and three meridians—the Ren Channel, Du Channel, and Chong (Vital) Channel—meet together. It is a very important point. It is in the center of the perineum, between the anus and the scrotum in males and between the anus and the posterior labial commissure in females.

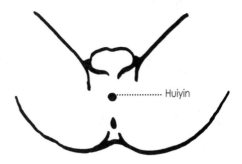

Yongquan

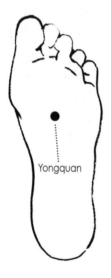

Yongquan

This acupuncture point is on the sole of the foot. The meridian energy moves up into the body from this acupuncture point, just as water springs from a fountain. This acupuncture point is very important, and it is considered as a second heart in Traditional Chinese Medicine.

Laogong

This point is in the center of the palm. It is a very important point in the treatment of diseases.

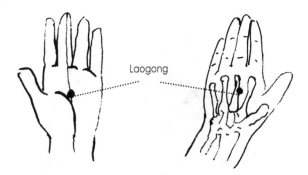

Laogong

Ch'i Hui

This point is right below the middle of the clavicle bone. It is the door to the respiratory system.

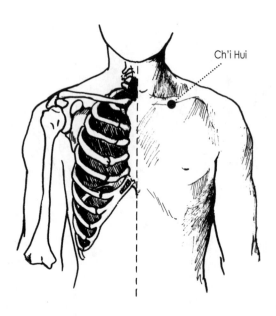

Ch'i Hui

Jingmen

This point is just above the waist behind the lower edge of the ribcage, on the back at side of the chest. This point is used to alleviate worry and terror.

Zhangmen

Front side point above the waist in front of the lower edge of the ribcage.

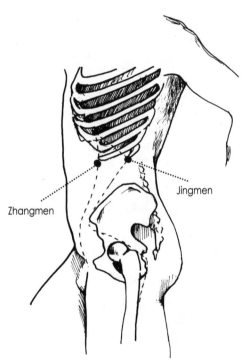

Zhangmen

Jingmen

INDEX

A

Active Kung, 32
anger, excessive, 9
arrow fingers, 87
asthma, 22

B

Baihui, 102, 137, 139
Bien Chiu, 119
blood, 19
　pressure, high, 19
bones, 26
breath, 10
　counting your, 34
　listening to your, 34
　regulating, 35
breathing Ch'i from the
　universe, 50
breathing
　favorable, 35
　free, 34
　genuine, 37

holding, 36
latent, 37
methods, eight kinds, 38
natural, 35
reverse, 36
bronchitis, 22

C

cellular activities, 17
cerebral cortex, 16
cerebral hemorrhage, 21
Changquian, 147
Chengjiang, 137
pouring the Ch'i twice, 59
Ch'i, 3, 5, 81, 111
　feelings, 17
　hui, 152
　three techniques of
　building, 10
Ch'i Kung, 3, 4, 5, 6, 13
　meditation, 14
circulation, 19